Wild Captives

Wild Captives

BY DONALD G. DODDS

Illustrated by
Ronald Andrews

MACMILLAN OF CANADA

TORONTO

Reprinted 1967

Library of Congress Catalogue Card No. 65-17064

Printed in Canada for The Macmillan Company of Canada Limited, 70 Bond Street, Toronto, by the T. H. Best Printing Company Limited

TO TRACY AND KATHY

Contents

Preface

Wild Captives was written during the winter of 1957-8 while I was serving as a provincial government wildlife biologist in Newfoundland. In the evenings I would write a story, or part of one, by the light of a kerosene lamp – partly for relaxation and partly to gain some perspective of the research problems I was dealing with. The stories are an attempt to show in a non-anthropomorphic way a part of the environment in which each animal lives. These are the animals' own lives in the wild. Man's influence on the individual animal, the environment, and the species is shown as a strong factor in the destiny of animal populations. I hope that the readers of this book will gain some appreciation of the important role man plays in determining the future of our wild animals, and some insight into the lives of the wild creatures that now share the environment with man.

DONALD G. DODDS

Wild Captives

CERVIER

The Lynx

The grey jay bobbed chirping from log to limb. Flittering noisily about him were two tiny kinglets. From his actions, the jay might have been playing a game of hide-and-seek with the smaller birds. Could he tell by their behaviour, perhaps, when he was nearing their nests? Or was he simply made curious by their incessant chirping?

Up from a rotting birch log into a young fir the jay hopped. He perched on a swinging limb and cocked his head mischievously while the kinglets kept up their cries.

Suddenly a robin flew from a near-by perch. The jay fluttered around the fir in furious escape. Round and round they flapped – chirping, squawking, screeching! Then the jay flew straight off and away from the fir-tree. On a distant birch the bird fluttered his feathers, chirped, and preened himself, looking indignant at having his composure so ruffled.

Back at the fir, the robin had a quick look at the tiny, throbbing young in its nest. Was this the real cause for the jay's presence? Had the clever bird been merely biding his time with the kinglets? Or was there still another attraction for a curious thief somewhere near this fir-tree and fallen birch log?

The birch log had been the main trunk of a great tree a few years before. Now, only the heaved, knotted roots remained, supporting a thick stub of dead wood. This stub, the fir, and

I

three young birches sheltered its tent-like roots.

Deep inside the darkened cavern below the great stump, another life was only a few days old. There, Cervier the lynx kitten lay in a ball asleep, while his mother padded about the edges of the neighbouring alder-bed in search of food. She would return shortly, for it was full daylight now, and the spring-like whistle of the fox-sparrows filled the morning world.

Perhaps the cat would tarry a bit to take a scratching sparrow as it flicked away the leaves and pecked for insects. Now many hundreds of migrant birds crowded about the alder-bed in search of their morning food.

The snowshoe rabbit fed in the open during the dusky evening and early morning hours, too. The earliest greens poking from the leaves between the puddles were choice fare after a winter's diet of woody twigs.

Indeed, the woodland moved with abundant life and the lynx could take what it needed to rebuild the weight lost during the late, lasting winter. Breeding and pregnancy had eaten away the fat during that period when food was scarce.

Lying motionless where the firs began their growth at the edge of the alders, the mother cat watched the feeding finches and thrushes. Her eyes opened and closed dreamily as the birds flitted about, sometimes so close that she felt the draught from their beating wings. She didn't move. She had eaten her fill earlier in the morning. A clinging feather still fluttered from her nose as she breathed. Three birds and a rabbit, caught with ease and eaten in peace during the early-morning hours, made her feel comfortable, and she dozed, a silent part of the noisy morning.

The first day Cervier's eyes were completely opened, he saw only light. Deep inside the cavernous nest it was dark; only the entrance was brightened. The lynx kitten swayed on wobbly legs and crawled about trembling as the mother cat washed him and herself. Her rough tongue tripped the kitten over each time she began to lick him. She would wait, and watch him regain his feet to wobble about again. The female paid much attention to the kitten, washing him even as he nursed. This year, as last, she had only one kitten, and she gave the single offspring all the attention she might have given two, or even as many as six, kittens.

It was easy for the mother cat to see her kitten in the den. Her eyes were filled with pupil while she lay within the dark recesses of the natal chamber. Outside in the bright sunlight her pupils would narrow to slits.

As a kitten, Cervier played a little, but not as much as he would have if he had had brothers and sisters. Sometimes the mother cat would play with the kitten for a while. At these times she would lie on her side and use one paw only to combat the bouncing, charging menace. Cervier liked to lay his ears flat on his head and sidle stiff-legged up to his mother, but her roughness in retaliation usually lessened his enthusiasm after the first few charges.

Cervier did not play with his food. Whether his mood was playful, sleepy, or watchful, he became serious when his mother dropped a mouse, a bird, or young rabbit on the floor of the den. From his very first mouse, Cervier would clench the food in his jaws and growl before trying to cut it with what would become sharp cheek-teeth.

By early July Cervier was playing about outside the den. The robins were nesting a second time now, and, although the mother cat knew they were in the young fir near the stump, Cervier had not noticed them yet. The first hatch had long ago dispersed, as had the tiny kinglets from their hidden home. The female lynx seemed to pay little heed to either group of young. Why was this so? Is it not strange that the predator should live in the midst of its prey and yet seldom harm it?

One dusky evening soon after Cervier had first ventured from the root home, he lay on the birch log resting. After frisky play, climbing the birch stump and digging his claws into the gnarled roots, he had subsided into this quiet mood. His face and ears were clean. Indeed, he was clean all over, for the mother lynx had washed him in the den, and, since coming out, Cervier had busied himself for a time washing clumsily but persistently. Emptied of play, and chores complete, he lay motionless with paws out straight, even, and side by side – his head held above them, senses alert to the early sounds of evening. Cervier was busy growing up to be a cat.

The woods swelled with choruses of veeries and hermits, their sharp, metallic warning clicks adding a staccato contrast to the smoothness of their songs. Mournful calls from the whitethroats and the sharp, coarse notes of the flycatcher complicated the harmony of the music. A few fox-sparrows and water-thrushes held on to the day, but their notes lacked the lustre of early-morning songs.

Cervier was not alone. There were all these birds and more. There were the rabbits and all the other mammals of the evening, and there was his mother, sitting behind him at the end of the big birch log.

Tonight, the mother cat would take her offspring with her as she hunted their daily fare. Cervier must learn to hunt and his mother must be the teacher. Already, the little cat crawled about in play with his belly-fur dragging over the ground as he stalked an imaginary mouse – a moving leaf or a waving plant. His jump was like his mother's killing leap in form, but less accurate, less powerful, and untimed. Cervier would have to learn patience. He must be able to time his leaps and capture his prey at one bound, for the lynx was not constructed for the chase. His longer hind legs, useful for quick and silent movement over the uneven forest floor, were ungainly for straightaway running. He hunted by working through tangled, brushy cover in search of a rabbit, or by lying in wait for an hour or more along a rabbit lead or other animal path until his meal moved unsuspectingly within reach of the sudden leap.

Cervier must learn to wait, to seek, to kill effectively. He must learn to stalk the gosling and even the goose, to find the nests, to catch the pool-trapped salmon. The lynx hunts at night. This is the time of roosting birds and feeding rabbits, and so the cats are adapted for a life in near-darkness. The eyes, ear-tufts, whiskers, and nose are their aids for night hunting.

Into the darkened forest night they went, mother cat followed by the tumbling, bumbling kitten. Occasionally the mother emitted soft noises as she called for Cervier to keep up. At these occasional calls she would stop, turn her head, and wait.

It was hard work for the kitten. Windfalls that the mother jumped with ease were obstructions for Cervier. Sometimes he would find an opening and crawl under a fallen tree instead of going over as the mother would. This took more time and brought a note of admonishment from the mother cat. But Cervier kept up. He did not fall behind.

The cats had travelled for twenty minutes or more when they reached a small alder-lined stream, branching from the brook that passed near their root-chamber. Along this brook the moose had worn a path, a winding path that branched often to form a conflicting maze of small trails. Rabbits, coming from the cover of the young firs at the edge of the alders to feed upon the green shoots of grass and sedge, would use this path and its branches during their feeding period. Knowing this, the mother cat lay down to wait beside the trail. Cervier stood beside her until she stood up and walked to a small group of firs a short distance behind them and called the kitten to her with a high purr. She wanted Cervier to lie down by the firs. He did so, and waited and watched, just as his mother, by the path, waited and watched. Outstretched on their stomachs they lay, their powerful hind legs ready to propel them through the air to the victim. Cervier would not make a kill from where he was, but he must mimic his mother now. He waited, as she did, ready to leap.

The northern forests in near-darkness are strangely silent. Calls of the soft-voiced creatures melt into the quiet night. The forest has expression, and her mood at nightfall is peaceful. So the occasional calls of the veery, the hermit-thrush, the great horned owl are calls of peace and of solitude.

These sounds the cat heard as she lay in wait. And other sounds, too. A branch breaks along the edge of the alder-bed a hundred yards below her! She hears hesitant movement – stopping, brushing through thick growth, and stopping again. The cat knows the sound of the moose which has come to the alder-bed for a meal. While the animal is still fifty yards away, the mother cat hears the gangling beast chewing its food.

Cervier is excited now. This cannot be what his mother awaits – or can it? Trembling, stretching his neck to look above the ferns and grasses, Cervier strains to see what makes the noises he hears. The moose moves out onto the trail and ambles slowly down the path, stopping occasionally to feed on the lush fern growth.

It is a bull, his antlers nearing full growth but covered with thick velvet. This is mid-July. Six weeks or a little more must still pass before the great animal will scrape the antlers to a glistening polish and join in the mating pattern once again.

When the animal came abreast of the mother cat, it moved its massive head slowly toward her for a few seconds before passing. Whether it sensed the cats' presence or not, neither Cervier, lying frightened but curious in the grass, nor the mother knew. The moose would often stop and peer at something, or nothing, during its nocturnal travels.

After it passed, Cervier sat up and stretched his neck to watch the hulking creature move away. Now that the danger seemed less, he could afford to indulge his curiosity and watch.

It was perhaps ten minutes after the moose had moved by them, though they could still hear it, that the mother lynx killed. A large doe snowshoe rabbit, heavy with her second litter of the season, leaped down the trail from the direction in which the moose had gone. She, too, stopped on occasion and moved her ears to gather in all the tiny sounds of the forest night. She is an expert at escape. Her ears, radar-cones of the wild, are attuned to the slightest of sounds. Her delicate nose can distinguish between all the species of herbaceous and woody growth in the forest she knows. The nose, too, can discern odours strange and unwelcome to the little sphere of the rabbit. Her eyes, on either side of her narrow head, show her the world that surrounds her at each instant.

The rabbit was staying close now to the form or lair she used during most of the daylight hours. She would venture only a few yards for green food, fresh twig growth, or cool water from the little brook. A few more yards down the path, she would turn to face her resting-place and feed slowly back.

Here was something dark in the path! She stopped, alert, stretched her neck out, and smelled, while still six feet away, the droppings of the moose that had so recently passed. Relaxed again, she brought her head back and sat for a moment, nose wriggling and working constantly. Suddenly she tensed. There was something else! Without seeing, hearing, or smelling it, she sensed something else. Then she gave a short 'click', hopped about to face the opposite direction, and screamed as she was at once covered with a dark weight and held by claws that pierced her flesh, heart, and lungs. There was no struggle, no pain, only a fleeting instant of fright.

The mother cat picked up the rabbit in her mouth. She could feel the delicate throb of life, the life of the doe's four unborn young.

Cervier stood rigidly, watching his mother come towards him with the animal in her mouth, and lay it on the ground before him. Curious at first, he smelled the warm fur and flesh, poking his nose about on it. In the root-chamber he had eaten rabbit many times. They were always still. This creature had been moving a moment ago and its scream had startled the young cat.

The mother licked her chops and washed her face as she waited. Her kitten, after deciding that the rabbit was harmless, grabbed the meal, growled, and began to chew at the head. With the warm odour of blood filling her nostrils and the sound of breaking bones in her ears, the mother stopped her washing, bent down, and smelled the rabbit's hind quarters. Cervier growled defiance and began to retreat slowly backwards, with the rabbit clenched tightly in his mouth. But the mother, her own appetite whetted, suddenly snatched at her kill. Cervier growled, spat, and sprang his claws as the female took hold of the prize, but a sharp slap cowed him into silent, watchful submission. The two cats shared the rabbit now, the mother chewing the rear part into two pieces as she ate. Cervier ate the head end, choking as he gulped it down.

Within the outward calm and richness of the life of the forest is an inward awareness of the presence of death. Death pads the forest floor as a lynx, patters across the marshes as a fox, glides through the blackened night as an owl, slithers from beneath the stump as a weasel.

The cats killed twice more before daylight. Cervier and his mother hunted the same path, resting and sleeping at intervals, alert even in sleep.

A baby robin had dropped from the fir-tree nest and lay pulsating on the ground near the root-chamber. Its eyes had opened and its voice was shrill. The little bird was becoming well feathered, but its feather tracts were still evident. The growth was not yet full enough to hide the sources from which all the bird's feathers would grow.

Bounding ahead of his mother as they approached the den, Cervier noticed the robin first. Quickly, he caught the helpless creature and choked it down as his mother approached.

She, sensing his kill, looked about on the ground for others. There were none. All the others were in the nest a few feet above. She climbed up now, reached to the nest, and tore it from the tree.

Throughout the summer, the two cats hunted together, Cervier gradually becoming more skilful but still somewhat impatient. They seldom used the root-chamber after mid-summer, and hunted farther and farther away from the birth-place. Now, in late September, they had wandered to where they could hear the mighty rumble of a waterfall day and night. They had not yet ventured to the falls together, but the female had often been here before. This was where the salmon spawned.

Here, shimmering salmon struggled to move gravel, lay and fertilize the roe in a succession of pockets, to repopulate that water and others with their kind. The water was cool and clear and, except for the spray pool beneath the falls, shallow. The water-level, so near the headwaters, remained stable. In this pool eggs would receive the oxygen they needed to hatch into fry. Here the circulation of the water was good and its temperature so cool that the eggs would not hatch until late spring; but eggs that hatch slowly produce life as healthy as eggs hatched in a short period.

The female lynx had chanced upon these spawning salmon years before and, though she had not fished before, she had been curious about the turbulence in the clear, shallow waters. For a long time she had watched the spawning fish and then she grabbed one as it writhed close to the shore where she lay. Its muscular snaps surprised and frightened her and she dropped it on the sand, watching it until the flopping subsided. Then she approached the fish, smelled it, and began to eat, releasing it and backing off at times when the still-living creature thrashed about. The taste had been pleasant, and after feeding on the fish past its death she covered it partly with sand and went to sleep in the bordering forest-cover. A bear visited the area in the early daylight and, sniffing out the half-covered delicacy, ate it. The lynx watched in silent disapproval.

She caught others after that fall day and sometimes even took the spent black salmon from the lower pools in early spring, for most fish do not begin their return to the sea until the ice has left the streams. Now, she brought Cervier to the spawning-pool as she had done with all her previous offspring.

Cervier and his mother remained near the spawning-pool for three days before moving a night's travel away. While they were there, Cervier learned to catch and eat salmon. This was a delicacy few lynx would ever chance upon, but fresh fish would be a natural part of Cervier's diet as long as he lived. If he happened to find trout or salmon from this time on, he would stay and fish. Another lynx might feed upon carrion herring or cod along the ocean-shore, or possibly on rolling caplin during the summer months. Many would never find either the carrion of the sea-shore or the salmon of the spawning-pools. It would depend upon their movements and their local food supplies. Cervier's travels with his mother had brought him into contact with the spawning salmon. He would probably return to this pool or find a similar one in the area he must soon choose to roam.

After leaving the pool, the two lynx spent nearly a full week a night's journey away. They fed upon mice in the grassy meadows of a once-flooded stream that had long ago been abandoned by beaver.

From the beaver-meadow they travelled in a wide circle, skirting the edges of the great hills that lay about their valley. Spending a day or two in some places and travelling by night, they fed on mice and rabbits or occasionally small birds. The migrant song-birds had flown far to the south, now, and only the residents remained. And, of the residents, it was the friendly, unsuspecting chickadee that most often fell victim to the hunting cats. Seldom were the little birds hunted with purpose. Most were taken as the lynx lay quiet during the early-morning or late-evening hours, waiting for a rabbit. Hopping on lower limbs or flying low over the un-moving lynx, the chickadee met its fate. With eyes and ears that missed almost no movement, the lynx would often spring into the air like a flash and catch the bird in its great clawed paws. Most chickadees passed unharmed, but when the cats were hungry or impatient they took the birds with purposeful, timed leaps. Cervier caught most of the birds. He was far more impatient than his mother and more than once spoiled a much better catch by leaping to take a bird, thus revealing his presence to a near-by rabbit.

With the first snows of early November, the circle was complete. The cats were near the home where Cervier had been born. During the fall, food had been plentiful. There were hundreds of thousands of rabbits and mice in the valley this year. Perhaps another year they would not be so easy to catch.

The cats' journey had taken them for many miles across rivers and ponds, through cut-over areas and virgin timber. The trip would serve a purpose some day, for Cervier must choose a hunting-ground of his own. He would not always hunt with his mother, though like most cats Cervier's mother would keep her offspring with her until early spring.

Both cats were now silvery with their long winter guard-hairs. The spots that showed so clearly on Cervier's coat when he was a kitten were now but faint suggestions, distinguish-able as spots only on his legs. Down his back was a streak of black hair, salted with silver. His sides, shoulders, and flanks were silver-grey and his stomach straw-coloured with silver tints. But, even with the beautiful first winter coat, Cervier still looked only half like a cat. His bob-tail and long hind legs dropped off too quickly. His body tapered down from his black-tipped tail to all the expression and personality of a lynx: his head. The face was the cat, the rest of the animal, nothing. Dark lines turned gently between the silver on his forehead and cheeks. Great black tufts stuck rigidly from his well-furred ears, and heavy jowl-brushes of silver and black trembled in fright or intimidation. Owl-shaped eyes, yellow-green balls dotted with countless dark specks centring in a razor-thin line of black which could fill the sphere at darkness, made the head alive. The nose was a dark red-brown, its perforated skin trimmed with a fine line of minute black hairs. It did not usually move by itself, but with the whole head. Whiskers on both sides were many-shaded from black to silver. They were thick and varying in size and spread wide from the face, reaching a point on each side that would clear the rest of the animal's body.

Kittens born later in the year than Cervier would have straw-coloured, silky hairs, much softer than Cervier's. Cervier's winter coat was really almost indistinguishable from the adult cat's, though it was not as heavy and the young cat was not as big.

As the snow built up over the ground, the two cats restricted their activity. Although their huge paws allowed them to travel through snows soft and deep, they found it more difficult than travelling over the forest floor, marsh, and bog. The route they now followed took them about seven miles in as many days and nights. Fat and content, they roamed slowly, hunting rabbits and occasionally taking a careless chickadee.

There were other lynx in the forests. Several times during the summer Cervier had smelled other cats, but his mother always avoided meeting them. Now, they often crossed and recrossed tracks of other lynx.

Early one day in late December Cervier and his mother lay only a few yards apart when a giant cat padded down the forest trail towards them. Cervier looked at his mother. She was watching the huge cat intently, not moving. The young cat trembled as the great tom approached. Straight towards Cervier it moved, approached to within a yard, stopped, and looked. Cervier pushed himself backwards and rose to his feet. He arched his back and his fur stood upright. His stub-tail shook and he twitched it in staccato movements. He stood his ground. The big tom stood for perhaps a minute, glanced at the mother who had not moved, and padded away through the fluffy snow.

Cervier was grown now. As a cat he was safe. He might not have been safe as a kitten.

The winter is long in western Newfoundland. Bottomless gulches fill to the brim with snow which in some places remains until snow comes again. On the barren country, wind sweeps the snow from the hill-tops into the valleys. All animals save the tiny mouse, the remnant caribou, and the hare leave the exposed area for shelter in the valley. Cervier's valley was deep with snow but heavily timbered, sheltered in many places, and safe from human visitors during the long winter. Plump white ptarmigan ran about the alder-beds feeding on twig tips and buds, and behind them, into the timber edges, came the fox. This influx swelled the valley's population during winter months and, though the ptarmigan was not a difficult bird to stalk, both fox and lynx stayed largely content with the many white rabbits to be had this year.

The sun shone longer as winter grew old, and with the lengthening days came the crust snow. March found the crust thick and strong. Cervier began to travel longer distances with his mother, and, suddenly, alone. One night, they met another male cat, and after travelling with them for two days he drove Cervier away.

Cervier hunted alone, just as he had hunted with his mother. Nosy, he poked into everything, whether he wanted to eat or not. He had always done so, just as his mother had done. Now it chanced that he came upon strange tracks a few days after separating from his mother. Long and wide, they webbed the light frost snow prettily atop the solid crust. He padded along in the prints. The wire hung in the path of the prints, and had there been a new moon no glint would have shone. With its sides snuggled behind small fir branches, only the bottom of the loop and the tie around the pole were visible even now. Cervier stopped and looked. There was no other place to push through. It was completely blocked off with small trees and branches. He sat down and watched. Nothing moved! One, two, three, five, ten minutes passed. Cautiously now, he moved forward, smelling, padding carefully. He slipped his head through, felt the wire just as it touched his delicate whiskers and then his throat. He backed up. The loop had slipped down and looked different. Something had changed. He walked quickly to the left of the slip, poked his head into the branches, and shoved his way into the clear.

Cervier's second summer was spent lazily travelling and hunting the area near the great river only a mile from the root-chamber. His mother had another kitten this summer, but though Cervier often crossed the area close to the old birch log the animals never saw each other. There was no longer a bond between Cervier and his mother.

He hunted mice and rabbits, numerous this summer, and poked his nose in all the curious little places along his travels. He yawned, stretched, cleaned his toe-nails, dug and scratched, washed, climbed the long, leaning trees, laid his ears flat and growled, trembled and shook; he covered his uneaten food with a few straws of grass and left his droppings on the same hummocks throughout the season. All these things and more he did within an area only a mile across, because food was plentiful. When food is not so plentiful, the lynx roams greater distances, and during early spring he may roam for miles, even with good hunting.

One night in early fall, Cervier came upon a curious group. Four lynx were sitting on a large, flat-topped rock, doing nothing, it seemed, but resting. They were not a family group, for all were adult animals, males and females who had not mated during the early spring. The females might mate yet, for young lynx are sometimes born during the cold days of mid-winter. Cervier joined the group for three days. They hunted rabbits together and caught many simply by startling animals into running inadvertently towards another lynx.

After Cervier left this group, he travelled alone for the rest of the fall and all of the winter. He spent days lying beneath windfalls as the winter storms raged relentlessly. He hunted rabbits and birds and travelled his country over a larger route, covering a mile or two or even six or seven miles each night, though game was plentiful. So, by early March, he was moving in a great circular route that brought him near the birch log every seven or eight days.

Then Cervier found a mate, a young female only as old as himself. She drove him back from intimate contact, snarling and throwing her well-armed paws, keeping him well away at each suggestion of closeness. He followed her at a distance that sometimes reached a hundred yards or more, all night long, through the next day, the next, and the next. Both made occasional noises, each sounding like a tom-cat howling a short howl into a tin can. Their tones differed slightly on this call and on the others – the low growls, the purrs, and the trembling cat-chatter. Always their tones were soft, except when the female, in anger, drove Cervier back. At these times she howled noisily and hissed and spat like a domestic cat, though much louder.

Cervier was nearly two now and he weighed about twenty-five pounds, perhaps seven pounds more than the female. His head was larger than hers and looked rougher and bushier than the smoother, more graceful female's.

Night after night they travelled in company, allowing their curiosity to take them into darkened corridors under windfalls, to rabbit snares set by men, and, once, into a cubby baited for lynx. They had been taking rabbits from snares occasionally as they travelled, and this set was made to foil them. The female did not enter over the raised stick at the cubby entrance, but Cervier did. He stepped over, scraped the pan of a trap, and sprang it harmlessly. This time he did not get caught, and, his curiosity satisfied for the moment, he backed out and continued on his way, following the female. The scent that had attracted him was sweet, and unfamiliar. It had been perfume – a scent belonging to the world of man.

In the first week of April they mated. The two animals fought and howled together for a full week and then remained paired, still hunting and snooping, until early May.

The third day of May was sunny and bright with the glare of the sun on the granular snow-crust. There was no snow on the trees now, but two feet of whiteness still covered the forest floor. The animals of the white hill country had been moving for several weeks. The rabbits, the foxes, the lynx had mated. The moose moved freely to the open areas in hopeful search of succulent vegetation, happy to be able to walk with ease on snowless roads or on marshes where the snow was fast disappearing. The straggling doe caribou travelled toward their fawning areas, heavy with young.

Cervier lay sleeping at the base of a small fir, shaded by a canopy of larger fir and birch for the whole of the daylight period. The female lay not far distant. They were contented, and bloated with old rabbits taken from slips that had not been removed at the season's end.

All around them the forest twinkled with the colours of migrating birds. Their songs lasted from daylight to dusk and even into the dark hours of the night. It was spring, when old life stirred to create the new.

That night, as the darkness slowly snuffed out the individual trees making the forest into a single black body, Cervier moved along a trail behind the female. She had jumped over a stick lying low across the trail. Cervier dropped his head a bit and walked under – part way. The slip tightened around his neck and he lunged ahead, clawed violently at his neck and the stick, pulled himself over the pole, and leaned back, resting with the wire taut. He pawed weakly and was still. Cervier was no longer a part of the living forest.

The female walked back along the trail to where the dead animal rested, partially suspended, on his haunches. His neck was twisted crudely, unnaturally, and one claw held his right paw to the wire where it had caught in a final feeble attempt to loosen the thing that had snuffed out his life in slightly more than a minute.

She walked around the body several times, approaching it twice. She sat and waited, watching it, making occasional soft howls. She waited for over two hours until the warm odour of life was spent, and then she left.

In the forest near by, the plaintive call of the white-throated sparrow interrupted the stillness, stopping on the second high tone as if the bird suddenly remembered that daylight had not yet come.

LEPUS

The Hare

This is a story of fear. Perceptions heightened by fear allow the snowshoe hare to live. Without fear the animal would soon become extinct.

Most of the mammals and birds in the northern forest belong to one of two great groups – predator or prey. The predator travels far, moving much of the time, to get its food. It is equipped to kill by teeth or beak, claws or talons. Some predators hunt by stealth, others are fleet afoot or swift flyers. All have highly developed senses to help them find their prey.

The prey is usually a more sedentary beast, feeding on plants. Prey creatures are equipped to escape. Some run fast. Others can 'freeze' and blend with the landscape. Many make use of burrows or trees or rock dens and crevices. Their senses are also highly developed, and they are afraid.

There are mammals and birds that may prey upon lower creatures or even others of their kind, yet themselves become prey for another larger or more efficient killer. These creatures, too, are afraid.

In the great forests and barrens of Newfoundland, there are few kinds of mammals. The predators are the lynx, the fox, the weasel, the otter, the few marten, the mink, and the shrew. The prey are the snowshoe hare, the muskrat, the mouse, the beaver, and the arctic hare. Very occasionally, a

18

weasel or a shrew becomes the prey. Of the larger animals, the bear may sometimes kill; the caribou and moose are seldom attacked – because of their size. Bats, which are flying mammals, seldom fall prey to the larger predatory beasts.

The snowshoe hare is an important link in this chain of killers and killed. Because hares are plentiful, they are the chief food of the fox and the lynx. There are few amphibians and no reptiles to be taken by predatory mammals or birds in the Newfoundland forests, so flesh-eaters live entirely on small quadrupeds and song-birds. Yet the numbers of snow-shoe hare are regulated not by animal killers but by man, who sometimes kills too few, and allows disease to run through the hare population and shrink it. He cuts the timber, removing protective cover, and when regeneration occurs the snow-shoe suffers through competition for food with the moose. It is man who alters the landscape in forestry and agriculture, mining and industry. He makes wet lands dry and dry lands wet. He hunts and kills, traps and kills, snares and kills, and kills and kills. Through ignorance or knowledge, by accident or reason, man directly destroys. Through long and complicated chains of events that must occur within the environment after man has laid his hand upon the land, also, he destroys.

Summer is heat hanging close to the bog, deer flies and wild bees, mosquitoes and black flies. It is a succession of flowering plants – rhododendron, lambkill, wild orchid; large and showy, wondrously tiny and inconspicuous. It is a series of hatches in the insect world and a period of restless activity for the bot-fly, the carrion beetle, and the saw-fly. Summer is pale green at the tips of fir branches. It is the heavy, pungent smell of Canada balsam and spruce gum. In summer, woody growth is clothed except where the moose has stripped the twigs. Green is everywhere. It is the world, save for the sky and the water.

Life increases in summer. It is full and it multiplies a thou-

sandfold. The young jay, hatched early in the spring, screeches beside its mother, crying to be fed, though it is as large as she is. The forests are almost crowded with tiny winter wrens, whitethroats and fox-sparrows, and a hundred other kinds of young birds.

In the plant world, seeds mature and ripen, to be loosed by the frosts and winds of early fall or picked and carried by the seed-eating birds of the land. In the water, fry become parr and millions of black-fly larvae cling to the rocks of rushing rivers and streams.

Cervier the lynx kitten travels with his mother and learns to live; the young foxes play and sometimes become almost serious in their outlook on life in so vast a world; the cow moose mothers her calf, thrusting her nose into the alder clump to nuzzle the resting young. Into this intimate frenzy of love, life, and death, Lepus is born. His mother sits on her haunches to give birth to a litter of four. She bore three young in early June and, somewhere about the alder-bed, one still lives. Two of her present July litter will survive until fall.

Lepus is born fully furred, his eyes are open, and within minutes he creeps about his mother, nuzzling for milk. For a few days the young hares are concerned only with milk and sleep. It is almost a week before Lepus fears the sounds, the movements of the wind, the objects about him. It is not death the creatures fear, for they know nothing of death. It is life they fear – and, at first, all manner of life. As they grow, they will begin to distinguish between sounds and movements and objects, and learn not to fear many. But at first there is nothing known to them and so they are afraid of all the world.

The female nursed her first litter for four weeks and weaned them soon after she became pregnant for the second time. Lepus will nurse much longer, for the doe will not be pregnant again this year. At first, after removing the foetal membranes, the doe nudged her offspring towards the teats, to induce them to suck. After the first day, the hungry, growing leverets feed whenever their mother lies on her side with them in the form.

The doe hare will nurse and lick her offspring less and less as they grow. Her first warning clicks are given when the young are only three days old, as they move a few feet into the tall grasses. As the periods of nursing are spaced farther apart, there are more warning clicks. Her maternal care changes, but it continues until the group is scattered by some outside intrusion, or until weaning.

Animals with smaller families — moose, bear, even lynx, otter, and beaver — care for their offspring much longer and more effectively. As breeding potential increases, maternal care becomes less efficient. The mouse, which produces so many so often, nurses its young only a few days, then crowds the nest with a new litter while the half-grown young forage on their own.

When Lepus was born, one hare in the litter was much smaller than the others. Its responses to the warning clicks were slower, and when the creatures froze it was always the smallest that resumed its feeding or movement first.

Early one morning, as the mist rose slowly from the dew-covered bog, a shadow of movement glided silently between the blue fog curtains above the feeding litter. The leverets froze as the click from the sensitive female preceded by an instant the appearance of the hawk. Lepus was motionless save for a tiny movement of his nose. He dared not move his great ears even to follow the sound of wings and air, and the sound of his throbbing heart deadened the surrounding world of life to him. Lepus remained still for a small eternity, for the doe knew that danger might not pass quickly and she repeated her warning.

The runt failed to respond to the second warning and in less than a minute resumed feeding, busily clipping and grinding the young stems of grasses and sedges. The hawk had glimpsed brown beneath him in flight and had pitched in the branch overlooking the bog's edge to wait for movement.

Down from the branch towards the leveret the talons dropped. The hare tried to escape, but it was slow to respond, even to danger. The bird pierced the hare on each side and pulled flesh from the pulsating neck with jerking slashes of a great hooked beak. At the shriek of the victim, Lepus scurried into the dense cover of the firs lining the bog edge and huddled trembling against the pole trunk of a low-branched tree. The others, the doe and the remaining leverets, were near by with him.

One leveret was gone from the litter now, and this was good – good for the kind, since the lost creature was slow and dull. It would not have been to the advantage of the species for that one to breed, and it was removed.

The shedding of leaves is a process of growth. Once each year, like the moose and its antlers, the tree rids itself of its withered foliage to make room for next year's crop of tiny food plants. Birch leaves, yellow now masking green, are picked easily and blown by the wind through forests dominated by the conifer green. Yet the evergreen also sheds its leaves. Far back on the branch the oldest needles drop to build on the mat beneath; and the larch turns yellow. Alive and green in the spring and summer, the larch seems each year to die when fall warns of coming winter.

Around the yellowing bog, the heath plants blaze many shades of red, orange, and yellow again. Scattered among the fall colours are a few late-blooming, purplish asters, not yet destroyed by the crystal nights which now leave thin coatings of ice over the tiny bog ponds for the eyes of early morning.

The forests are no longer alive with migrating birds. Only a few late-flying robins still remain with the birds of the northern winter. On the barrens, the bear feeds on the frost-sweetened berries, and the caribou gather to mate.

In mid-September one leveret is caught in a wire left from last year's snaring season, leaving Lepus and one female from the litter of four. Lepus weighs two and a half pounds by October the first and is still growing. He will reach three pounds or more before the snow falls.

With the yellowing of herbaceous growth, the grazing animals turn to browse. Lepus nips the choicest young shoots of birch, dogwood, raspberry, and a score of other woody plants available to him. Because his diet has changed, the young hare must range farther to find the tenderer plants. As Lepus travels the same route from day to day, the moss beneath the trees becomes compacted and a path is formed. Even the tiniest plants along the path are nipped, to clear the trail completely of growth that might brush roughly against the hare's coat. Then one night Lepus travels in another direction for food and returns several nights in succession until a second path is formed. This path cuts across the one used by other hares and gradually a complex, interlocking maze of paths results. This year there are many hares.

Another change is occurring now. Lepus is no longer a brown creature with a grey-brown belly and a white spot on his forehead. Now he is mottled with white. At first only his hind legs whiten, but soon his forelegs begin to turn colour as new growth succeeds the brown summer hair. By mid-October he is almost white, though brown hair shows lightly beneath the white guard-hairs, which will not cover the animal completely until December.

Man, too, changes his movements and appearance in fall. Now, jacketed against the coolness, he walks about the woodland, skirting the edges of bogs looking carefully for the paths that mark the presence of snowshoe hares. In these paths he sets slips of wire and catches many hares by the neck.

The hum of chain-saws resounds through the forest not far from Lepus. When he first heard the sound in early winter, he dared not move until long after dark, many hours after the noise stopped. Now he has become almost accustomed to this new sound and he leaves his form earlier. It is no longer easy for Lepus to find food. The snow is deep and settled and he must follow his paths to the end and travel over the heavy snow to find enough tender shoots to satisfy his hunger. Tonight he moves slowly along a path well known to him, stopping often to listen and judge the forest sounds and smells. Suddenly the path is blocked; it is no longer familiar. Lepus moves out of the path amidst the many branches of a newly cut birch-tree, felled by the woodsmen to clear the way for hauling their pulpwood. There is much food here and Lepus browses carefully, selecting the tenderer tips and nipping the finely scaled buds that might have been leaves in another spring.

There are other hares feeding here also. Two, three, four more soon join Lepus, and he knows one is the doe that bore him. The crash of a branch startles the feeding animals and they freeze, but only for seconds, for they recognize the pad of the giant moose moving through the forest snow. The moose comes up to the birch and begins to browse.

Next year, when the canopy of evergreens has been removed, there will be no protective cover for the hares in winter, and they will leave the area where Lepus and many others now live. Yet the moose will continue to feed, as young, succulent growth appears, and in feeding will retard the new trees. It will be many years before the hare returns.

Once, before the snowshoe hare or moose came to this forest, great arctic hares roamed the woodlands to the coast. Down from the barrens in late winter and spring they flooded the valleys and clipped the wild raisin, maple, and birch. Then came the snowshoe; its increase forced the arctic hare to the highlands. With the coming of the moose, competition increased, and now these browsers from the mainland fringe the native arctic hare's restricted home and, indeed, penetrate it.

Tonight as Lepus feeds on the birch across his path there are no arctic hares within his range. Man brought the snowshoe and the moose, and so lost the native hare. And man felled the birch and set the slip which now snuffs out the life of the doe that mothered Lepus. Her shrieks slice through the forest night as she forces her powerful hind legs to thrust her free and draws the noose tighter around her neck. Lepus and the others scurry swiftly away down the paths to the shelter about their resting-forms, and the moose trots away through the deep snows until it can no longer hear the fearful cries. A threatening, lonely silence follows.

But the winter night is still young. The many hares this year provide nourishment for the predators and hunting is easy. The snowy owl has appeared from far to the north where his food is depleted. He sits in the single birch left along a woodsman's cut-line, listening for sounds of movement. The shriek of the doe drew him, but now the doe is dead and movement has ceased.

Cervier the lynx walks across the near-by bog. He, too, has heard the cries of the hare and will investigate. It is easier to feed upon still creatures with the warmth of life within them than to catch the fearful prey alive. Moving cautiously, peering into every darkened place, the lynx hunts by the full moon of the late, cold night. Every track is investigated as the cat pads criss-cross over the newly cut land, sitting at times by piles of pulpwood. Cervier is in no hurry and, in fact, is not particularly hungry, yet he moves ever closer to the dead doe and in time reaches the creature warm with life, in death. He eats the hare while lying on his belly, slowly chewing the meat and bone, stopping to paw the carcass and roll over in half-hearted play. Cervier finishes all but the stomach, intestinal tract, and one ear. He moves to the edge of the bog and lies to rest by a hare path.

One young hare has lost weight this winter. Since her intestines were crowded with tapeworms, she did not grow as fast as most of the young hares during the fall season, or accumulate as much fat. Now she moves from her form to feed. The others here will not travel again this night. Cervier waits until the young doe is close to his resting-place, and lunges.

The hare shrieks once. The cat's great teeth have pricked the brain. Cervier draws his ears close to his head and trots with the rabbit a few feet into the low firs at the edge of the bog. He will eat only part of the animal but this one will be mauled. It is a trophy of the hunt, a prize, quite unlike the snared doe.

The owl glides from the birch and swoops low over the sounds it has heard. As it sails a few feet above predator and prey, it sees the lynx lift its head and hears the cat chatter. The owl must find another hare away from here tonight and before morning he will be successful.

Still another creature of the night sits motionless on the far side of the bog. Vulpes the fox was drawn by the cries of the doe in the snare, but his keen nose told him of the presence of Cervier and he has been sitting for an hour watching and listening. Vulpes does not fear the lynx but he is endowed with much caution. He would not have come closer to the snared rabbit even if Cervier had not been present. With the cry of the second hare, Vulpes turns and trots down the hill into the brook valley. His stomach, too, is full of hare.

Late in March Lepus clips alder-shoots by the tiny stream that leads from the bog. It is a moonlit alder-bed and two other hares feed near by. The nights are still very cold and the snow crusts hard at the beginning of each darkness. For the past week Lepus has been travelling a quarter of a mile or more in one direction to feed.

After a while the two hares that have been clipping coppice-growth shoots close to Lepus are side by side. One stretches its neck and sniffs of the other's tail and the female jumps about quickly and faces the buck. As the hares face each other their ears are bent slightly forward and each rubbery nose moves quickly up and down. At intervals of a few seconds the animals chew bits of twigs still held within their cross-cut jaws. It is several minutes before the buck stretches his neck forward cautiously. The doe then moves her head slowly and the noses of the animals touch, but only slightly, almost brushing. At this near-contact the doe leaps off the ground and turns running at great speed about the alder-bed, and the buck pursues. Lepus lifts his head and watches, and chews the bark he holds. Around the alder-bed they race, and back, and then towards Lepus. As the doe crosses before him, Lepus gives chase – and at once there is a tumbling of hares as the first male strikes Lepus from the side with his forefeet. For tonight the chase is over.

Movement increases in the hares' world. Each night Lepus is more active. He travels farther, eats less, and runs for great distances. For several nights he has met and chased a female larger than he. Each chase has ended with the doe striking out at the young buck with her great forepaws. During the day Lepus rests in a form near the female.

But the doe will not always run. One night she will stop and the animals will mate – once, twice, five times, or more.

With the first greens of spring, the hares begin their change in diet. Lepus comes upon tiny light green bulrushes along the rabbit-catcher's path, and clips a fragile shoot. Tiny rosettes appear, pushing up between snow patches that are now only groups of ice crystals. Soon the brittle-heads show their curled-up canes and the skunk-cabbage pokes a sturdy arm towards the sky. Spring comes and the browsers bid farewell to woody growth to put on fat from greens.

The does are burdened with their first litters in late April, and spring with its heavy rains threatens the tiny lives that will soon struggle against the odds of death. Weather is only one factor that can help or destroy the young hares. They may be killed by sickness or snares, by lynx or fox, by hawks or owls. For some, death is a house-cat, a truck, a shot from a gun. Fire may kill directly or reduce the food supply and remove the cover. The wood-cutter and the moose can combine to destroy the range.

And now the hares change coats. As the snow disappears, the white creatures become pied and finally brown, against the dull, colourless, early spring. This is not always so. Often the snow leaves early and the hares, still white-coated in a grey-brown country, are destroyed by predatory birds and animals alert to variations of colour.

The number of hares in summer depends on reproduction and survival last season and many years before. For the past four seasons productivity has been increasing. This summer's density will be the greatest in several years. In spite of predators and all the other decimating factors, the hares have increased. They will become so numerous by early September that a great many will die.

When the land becomes too crowded, the animals die until their numbers are once more compatible with the vegetation that is their home. Still a mystery to man, this disease of numbers prevents the hare from destroying his own habitat. Densities do not always approach the saturation level that triggers such stress within the population. Often a bacterium, a protozoan, or a virus reduces the count first. Sometimes the hares starve because food is scarce. Sometimes man and the wild predators combine to keep the numbers from increasing. Then the population fails to reach peak densities for another year or more. Over many centuries, snowshoe fluctuations in numbers average almost ten years between population peaks, though it has sometimes been less and sometimes much longer. Each species has a distinct fluctuation pattern that depends on its gregariousness, breeding potential, mobility, and environment.

Lepus survives the late-summer disease. Hopping about the paths beside the bog's edge, he comes across many hares dead and dying throughout September. He sniffs each one that is still and his only response is to wash his face unnecessarily or flick his ears when there is no tick. But the dying animals frighten him by moving unnaturally and Lepus responds by running to escape, and even with the running Lepus is still not stricken, and lives.

By living, Lepus increases his chances of dying. Each escape reduces the odds in favour of further escapes, each day shortens the closing life-span.

In his second fall Lepus is the only rabbit remaining from litters produced about the bog the previous season. Young of the present year are also few, following the great decline. This winter will be hard on the predators, and small birds and mice will suffer because snowshoes are scarce. For all the forest creatures, winter holds increased danger. Food is harder to find for both predator and prey and their bodies lose weight as stored energy is released over the long, long days of cold.

Lepus is fat as winter approaches. He is large for an adult male snowshoe, weighing over four pounds. No other hares feed this year on the new birch shoots, and, on his regular forays down paths to the raspberry cane, Lepus is alone. The path network through the young fir cover is not so extensive and the trails are not packed so hard as last year. Sometimes, between snows, Lepus hardly clears the side paths, and, as the winter wears on, he jumps over branches he would have run under the year before.

Lepus rests in his form, feeling the sun's warmth. For an hour or more each day, Lepus is warmed by the sun, in this form only partly covered by the spreading branch of the young black spruce. On an earlier day Lepus reached up and nipped the tip end of the branch. On stormy days he lies in the firs protected from the wind. Often he is covered by the fluffy snow before the storm ceases and the snow helps to contain his body's heat.

Lepus becomes aware of Vulpes when the fox is still in the firs thirty feet away. A waft of air carrying Vulpes' odour reaches the hare's delicate nose. The nose stops moving and Lepus adjusts his hind feet with a faint suggestion of movement. Lepus does not turn his head, but his ears move slightly as the fox glides closer. Vulpes stops at an opening behind the hare, barely fifteen feet away, and turns towards the frozen form. Lepus springs from his rest with a powerful thrust of steel-muscled legs and covers ten feet with each bound as he flashes through the firs into the alder-bed and circles back. Vulpes gains as the hare circles, for the fox cuts across the alder-bed, and, when the hare dives into the dense fir growth again, Vulpes is close and Lepus dies.

Interlude

MAMSHET

The Beaver

The water behind the dam is still. Along the pond's edges heavy dew bends the sedge blades toward the mirror surface. Occasionally the diamond beads drop, making tiny wave-rings form and disappear. The morning sun melts a covering haze, and drying begins. Morus, the mouse, scurries along ground trails beneath the leafy alder canopy. He clips and feeds and leaves little piles of criss-crossed green at intervals behind him. There are many thousands of mice now, down through the alder-bed and along the stream banks between the dam ponds.

It is late July and the warbler songs no longer crowd the morning air with proclamations of tiny domains, yet some still sing, and warning clicks occasionally sound from thrush and sparrow to remind the world that summer is still in the land.

The home pond is seven feet deep along the old stream channel. Trout lie thick near the bottom, hidden from all eyes of the air and land, for the bog water is dark. Now, the pond quiet is broken as a trout breaches; a gentle lap sounds and, soon after, another. The trout are feeding for a second time since daylight began.

Far to the rear of the pond, amidst the flooded alders, a brood of green-winged teal glides across the water surface. The female nested near the pond a year before, and this year

returned those many thousands of miles. Barring death, she will return again.

The beaver lodge on the north bank shows green leaves from a few freshly cut alder branches. These branches and a few globs of mud mark the beginning of an annual ceremony of repair and storage.

Six years ago the adult beavers of the home pond built a small dam only a few rods above the woods road and, with chance favouring them, survived until spring. That year they enlarged the dam and constructed a second lodge which they moved into with their first kits. Most of the available birch and mountain maple was cut and stored in two food piles that year. The following year the adults moved up-stream with their new kits while the middlers travelled down the watercourse. A second dam formed a pond home for two more years, and then the present pond was made. Now, two miles from the road, the beavers are in an area of rich vegetative reproduction from previous forest cuttings. Behind the alders, cut and floated for dam and lodge, grow the maple, birch, cherry, and the favoured aspen. If the beavers stay and live they will have food for several years.

Mamshet ventures from the lodge very little. He swims slowly yet, and cannot stay under water because his baby fur keeps him afloat. At first he stayed near his mother and mimicked her movements learning to swim. Now he goes alone or with his two sisters. Following the parent ways, they carry small sticks about in their strong-boned jaws and Mamshet has a small pile on the shore which he has removed from the lodge.

The slide down the dam-face to the bubble pool below was made by Lutra the otter who often visits the pond for trout. Lutra may den there in the spring when her first pups will be born. Now the old male beaver cracks a paddle tail on the water and swims toward the lodge. Short of shelter, he stops and turns in the water to face the dam. There is movement on the dam crest. Vison the mink, newly come to the land, is making his first visit to this stream. The teal that have been circling outside the alders to the dam swerve and glide away into the alders.

Vison eases into the water and swims in a short circle, then dives and returns to the dam where he climbs to a high point and sits on a stick, holding his front feet up before him. The teal have disappeared, but several wakes describe their pathway. Vison dips into the pond once again and is hidden from above. The old beaver submerges with a splash and soon the pond tremors settle. Then suddenly the surface becomes alive with thrashing birds as the teal skitter across the pond to the dam, clumsily claw their way over the top, and drop to the stream below. As the last bird drops over the edge, Vison surfaces at mid-pond and turns his head about. He will settle now for a trout.

Early evening finds Vison gone. The teal are back, and Mamshet's parents are working about the pond's edge. A bittern stands at one corner of the dam, and the beavers pass close but do not notice.

To learn, Mamshet must mimic. He swims out from the lodge to follow the adults but turns back midway across the pond and climbs on the slope of the lodge and sits. He rubs his forelegs across his belly until the male parent swims by, minutes later, carrying an alder branch for the dam corner. Mamshet follows and moves close by the male, pushing the branch against the dam with nose and forepaws. The adult moves away to cross the pond and Mamshet again follows only to return after swimming half way.

Beaver kits stay close to the lodge until the spring following their birth. Their early travels are along the shore, and here Mamshet first discovers the stick dam. He travels more often and farther than his sisters during the first summer. The food piles near the lodge make travelling under the ice barely necessary during winter, but the need to get food occasionally forces all the beaver to travel up-stream and on land during the weeks of late spring.

The second year following his birth a strange thing occurs. His parents have stopped looking after him and have become slightly aggressive towards him. The lodge is crowded. Mamshet and his sisters move in the spring season.

Mamshet swims up-stream from the lodge, crosses overland to another stream, and travels down. He encounters two occupied colonies and is driven on by their owners. On his fourth day of travel he comes to a wide river and, passing through one colony area, he heads up-stream and chooses the mouth of a small stream as home. Here he lives in the ice-hollowed bank with a small stick dam across the stream mouth. Twice it is washed away and twice Mamshet rebuilds. Mamshet survives the winter and in the spring the woodsmen blast his dam so they can run pulp sticks down his small stream. The young adult beaver moves on up the great river to the wide backwater and finds a mate.

The home pond is empty this spring. It was trapped clean during the winter. The parents were kept for fur and the drowned kits thrown into the alders where Cervier and Vulpes came upon them.

ALCES

The Moose

The cow moose moved from the thicket of budding alders lining the river-bank into the shallows and stopped. She turned her head towards the beaver lodge down-stream as the light lap of water from the swimming beaver crept an inch up her sturdy legs, rolled back, then crept up again. For several minutes the movement of water against her leg held her attention in the direction of the beaver lodge. No air stirred on this cool and dusky night. The water had been motionless only moments before. A few hundred yards above the lodge it still mirrored a perfect, darkening image of scattered clouds now salted with starlight.

Algen listened. She recognized delicate sounds as the movements of the beaver, but curiosity made her attentive. One of the beaver moved up-stream towards her. With its head breaking the water into a perfect shimmering V, it swam smoothly abreast of the moose as Algen turned slowly to follow the movement. Mamshet stopped swimming and lay quietly watching his audience for a few seconds, then swam on. Algen began to wade slowly deeper into the clear spring river. The snow had only recently abandoned the forests, leaving the world once again to the renewed and the unborn. A week ago, the river still flowed above its banks in many places. Now lowered, nearly to its normal flow, it had left masses of debris along its banks and about the bases of the alders. Early summer rains would mat this debris and great green fronds would combine with slender stems of sedges to mask its ugliness.

Algen began to swim as she moved farther from the littered bank. The strong and steady current eased her downstream and her wake formed an irregular curving bow as it settled below her and disappeared. She headed for an island in the middle of the river, an island no more than 200 yards long and perhaps a hundred yards wide, dense with yew, wild raisin, and mountain maple on the forest floor. A canopy of birch and fir sheltered these plants and a lush fern growth would soon appear in every available opening in the understory.

As her feet scraped bottom near the island shoreline, Algen raised herself from the water. She stumbled and splashed her feet and legs about for balance before reaching the heavy sand beach. Once on steady, dry footing, she flicked her ears, shook her mane, and wrinkled the heavily haired skin along her back and sides. It was several minutes before she moved slowly into the dense island cover, stopping to bite the tips of a young mountain maple that grew on the lower edge of the sloping water-torn bank.

It was mid-May in the valley of the Upper Humber River. Each spring on or within a day of the twentieth of this month Algen gave birth to a single calf. Like most moose, she never had twins, although she had often seen twin calves with other cows. This year she moved to the calving site as usual and spent six days wandering aimlessly to the shoreline and back to her concealed resting-place, stopping occasionally to feed.

Alces, a lanky, spindly-legged, reddish-brown calf, was born shortly before daybreak. He had large brown eyes, rather long floppy ears, a slight ridge of vertically patterned mane hair, and a tiny, wriggling stub tail, so short that the young moose, like his mother, looked almost incomplete. He was a miniature of his mother except that his head was

proportionately shorter and lacked a bell. Beneath Algen's chin and neck hung a wisp of skin covered with longish hair. All adult moose have these bells in varying sizes and shapes. Some hang to the ground, others are heavy, thick, and short. Even Alces had the very early beginnings of such a bell, and, as he grew, the dewlap would develop into a definite shape that would help distinguish him from other moose.

Alces slept a great deal during the first few days of his life. At times his mother would leave him for as long as two or three hours while she foraged for food. When she returned, he would be hungry and would suck until his belly bulged hard.

The place Algen had chosen to calve was in the midst of an extremely thick bed of ground hemlock interspersed with second-growth balsam fir. The yew grew high here on this fertile island, to well over four feet. In this dense coniferous bed Alces was safely hidden from man and beast. Algen was casual in her movements, so that any creature watching would take her to be feeding aimlessly – bent on browsing, nothing more.

When Alces was ten days old he began moving about the island with his mother. As Algen browsed the bursting buds, Alces would pick daintily at many things about the forest floor that to him appeared to be food. When something tasted unpleasant Alces would open his mouth, drop his head, and shake it from side to side as he protruded his tongue to spit the thing out. As his senses sharpened, he no longer made these errors. He grazed on the leaves and shoots of trees, bushes such as mountain maple, wood ferns, and other small plants. At the same time, he still nursed and would continue to nurse until early fall when his mother refused to nurse him any longer.

One day in June, Algen decided to leave the island for the eastern shore of the river. As he had done for nearly every day of his young life, Alces followed his mother about the island during the hour of daybreak, feeding on early green leaves, sedges, and ferns. But instead of going back to one of their resting-places as she usually did, Algen began to move into the water. At first, expecting his mother to return, Alces stood watching from the shore. Algen moved deeper and deeper until only the top of her back and head showed above the surface, then looked back and called softly.

Alces grew excited. He ran and pranced about the shore-line, lifting his forelegs high and stamping them down deliberately. His ears were laid back, almost flat, as he threatened imaginary nothings to his right and his left and on the ground before him. His mother's calls became more frequent and he watched her swim short circles and return to the same point. But Alces only pranced harder and even ran to the woodland cover of the island he now knew so well, circled, and returned – once, twice, three times. At last he stopped near the water's edge and looked towards Algen. Then, slowly, cautiously, retreating several times before moving into the water to his knees, Alces inched towards his waiting mother.

But just as he reached her, the water became too deep! Alces struggled. His front legs flailed about his mother's rump, grasped her tightly about her rear quarters, and then, as he moved his hind legs in a frantic effort to climb to more complete safety, Algen moved into deeper water and began to swim. Alces stopped struggling and hung on tightly with his forelegs. Across the river Algen moved with her calf, carried down-stream slowly as she swam. When she felt earth and stone under her feet she rose up to her height and walked, dumping Alces into water still too deep for him to touch bottom. He was forced to thrash his legs and swim, barely holding his head above water, for a few feet until he, too, reached the safety of dry land.

Many times Algen would repeat this process throughout the ensuing weeks as she swam and fed about the area of aquatic plant growth where the river widened above the island. And soon Alces would swim alone.

One day Alces had been frisking about his mother as they travelled together – charging her, threatening with mighty gestures, waving an antlerless ear-flattened head and showing the whites of his eyes – when their movement brought them to the edge of a river backwater filled with lilies, spatter-dock, and pondweeds. Out in the water they fed upon these plants growing in abundance. They had been feeding slowly for several minutes when a great commotion attracted their attention.

Moving through a narrow strait in the backwater, between two encroaching bog formations, came a noisy family of otters. Splashing, diving, and grunting, they churned the water to bubbles along their staggered pathway.

An otter family leads a playful existence. Although they must fish hard for the trout and young salmon that abound in the waters of the Upper Humber River, and forage many hours along the banks and bottom of the shallow channels lining the river here for larvae of aquatic insects, their work is turned into play. The successful otter pup must fight and flee to keep his captured trophy from brother and sister, for what one has the others want.

Algen and Alces had chosen a place to feed only a few feet from an otter rock in this quiet water. Here the otters would climb, their coats at once glistening dry in the morning sunlight, to eat their catches. They struggled with one another greedily for each trout, the victor crunching the head bones quickly down, only partly chewing the remainder of the soft-bodied food. Like others of the weasel family, the otters sometimes closed their eyes while eating, and the knowledge of this trait often meant success to the otter-hunter when the pelts were prime and the market good. Here, however, the otters had little to fear during the spring and summer as they fed, slept, and played about the back-water.

To the otter family, the watching moose were an interesting diversion. Diving and surfacing around the ungainly giants, they grunted and blinked, talking among themselves. They showed no fear and continued to fish between periods of observation.

The trout has little chance of escape from an otter in open water. Swimming in a straight line, the otter easily overtakes the fish. Only as the trout turns can it gain time to live, yet it never turns enough. Its only way of escape is to hide in weed growth.

Alces would soon grow used to seeing and hearing otters by day or night. Yet the thrashing of playful otters at their slides or in the pools was but a small part of Alces' world of sound. As morning broke, the twilight creatures, among them other moose in the backwater, made movement and feeding noises. The water slushed as the moose moved his legs and splattered as it dripped from plants torn from the oozy bottom. Ducks splashed and then broke a silence in the air with the beating of their wings. The early-morning snipe winnowed. Beaver travelled from lodge to lily-beds, the kits daring to travel farther each morning. Muskrats nibbled submerged buds of yellow lilies and trimmed the growing sedges, nourishing themselves to produce their litters. The noises from the actions of each mammal or bird were separate and important and Alces knew them.

The first song-bird of the morning is the whitethroat singing his repetitious, plaintive song. But soon he is joined by the fox-sparrow, the purple finch, the water-thrush. Then the sun begins to dry the crystal webs of morning and warm the air, destroying the mists. The early-morning songs fade and are replaced by the sounds of tree-warblers, wild bees, and ravens.

As evening approaches, the earliest sounds of daylight are often repeated, yet the thrushes, fox-sparrows, and whitethroats dominate the bird world, until night envelops the wild land and the dusky noises slowly, gracefully fade to the occasional call of a horned owl, and, always, the forgetful whitethroat.

Alces distinguished all these sounds – and the singing of the wind, the trickling of the brook, the thundering of the waterfall, the snap of a limb, the roll of thunder. And there were others, from fox kits, weasel, and bear, from dying hare, from feeding trout. As the sounds were distinctive to the moose, so were the smells, and, more dimly perhaps than these, the sights.

Early summer passes into summer; late summer into fall. In Newfoundland the time of warmth moves swiftly, hurriedly, through the season of growth. It is but a moment from bud to fruit. By mid-September the first frosts have often blanketed the forests. Alces seldom nursed now, for his mother was refusing him; at first she was only impatient, but now she was almost determined. The cow and calf had long since left the backwater area and had moved a mile away to the woodland second growth following a recent cutting of the pulp-woods by lumbermen. Instead of aquatic plants, which had grown less palatable as summer grew old, the moose now fed upon sedges and woody twigs.

Algen and Alces ranged over a larger area now. During the warmer months they had stayed near the backwater, spending much time lying in the wet marshes or standing in the cooling river. Since flies were less troublesome late in the season, they seldom went to the river now. Below them lay a woods road. Lately the two moose had spent much time in the cut-overs bordering this road. Here they fed during the early-morning and sunset hours, resting the remainder of the time, except for occasional nocturnal forays in the more open areas of young fir growth.

Suddenly a gunshot frightened Alces. He trotted at once a few yards and stopped, his ears flattened, head high. He looked back at Algen, standing with her neck arched towards the ground. The second report sounded and Algen's lower jaw dropped as if hinged, and waggled loosely. A third thundered through the woodland. Algen hunched her back and swayed. She spread her legs wide to support her weight. The fourth and fifth reports sounded. Algen folded slowly to the ground.

Alces moved uncertainly in a half-circle, testing the wind. He trotted towards his mother, then retreated. Five slugs, a knife, and an ax were the difference between Algen, the female moose mothering her spring calf, and four quarters of meat sold at fifteen dollars a quarter.

Alces was alone. He did not leave the area. There was food and heavy cover near by for refuge during periods of high wind or rain. These were adequate, and no other necessity dictated the calf's movements. Yet now there was a difference, for he no longer followed.

The moose calf takes no part in the breeding activity its first fall. Even if its mother mates, the calf is driven off only a short distance and for a short time, if at all. Alces found companionship with another moose calf not long after he had been orphaned. At first the mother of the calf had constantly intimidated him, driving Alces away. Soon, however, the cow became more tolerant and the two calves remained close to her until mid-October, when she mated. Though they were not forced to remain apart, the cow's new indifference and Alces' increasing independence caused the two calves to move farther from the cow, to feed, rest, and sometimes play by themselves.

Winter came with its snows, wind, and frost. Alces and his companion remained alone together until the heavy snows of December. Then, moving along a deeply cut path through the second-growth firs, they one day chanced upon six moose together in a stand heavy with birch, aspen, and fir within reach of the animals. Alces preferred the tips of aspen during the winter and this hardwood browse was a pleasant change from the heavy fir diet. The calves yarded here with the other animals. Moose are tolerant, even sociable, during the trying days of winter.

But these days pass. The storms, deep snows, crusts that cut the legs, slush, ice, and bitter cold are a part of life in the wild. A few of many species, weakened or old, may fall, but only a few.

With the melting snows, roads and trails become free of snow. Lengthening days swell buds and as spring approaches the moose become restless. Freed from the bounds imposed by winter's strong grasp, the ungainly creatures explore unfamiliar areas. All animals move at this time. Some, like the lynx and hare, increase their activity to find mates and breed; some, like the caribou, move to fawning grounds and summer range. The moose moves because it is free.

Though unaware of any change in his appearance, Alces *was* changing. Two rounded knobs, his first antler growth, stood out from his head, inside and to the front of his great long ears. Alces' companion had no such growth. The two animals roamed the Humber Valley together, exploring valleys, roads, trails – even buildings. They stopped to gaze at piles of pulpwood, trucks, and men. Yearling curiosity made them reckless and careless, yet they were not molested.

By midsummer, Alces' spike antlers were approaching full development. Covered with soft velvet tissue providing nourishment for the bone within, they looked for all the world like growths of brown moss.

During the summer, Alces once again spent much time near the backwater where, as a calf, he had learned to feed on succulent aquatic growth. Now, with the yearling female, Alces swam, fed, and rested in this area well known to him. The otters were there again, the ducks with their broods, the beaver, and the muskrat. In this world, as in the world of spring, fall, or winter, Alces was at home.

Each season adds strength to the growing children of the wilderness – strength in body, in the knowledge of friend and enemy, in adaptation to change.

Alces changed with the seasons. In the spring, and again in the late summer and early fall, he changed his coat. He changed his diet and movements as necessity dictated. He experienced an annual cycle of antler growth and his entire system changed as the autumn breeding season neared.

After they left the backwater in late August, Alces and the female often encountered groups of male animals. Occasionally they would attempt to join a group but, though at first the older males would tolerate the yearling male, they soon turned on Alces, butting him from the rear or putting much larger heads and antlers against his and shoving him backwards. As Alces drew away, the female, from a long association with him, would follow.

By early September the pre-rutting activity of the males was under way. Alces instinctively challenged males as he met them and continued to struggle against unequal odds to establish himself in the herd pattern, but yearlings are outcasts in this ceremony and from constant defeat the young moose soon learned his status. He rubbed the velvet from his antlers and stayed with the female, somehow content with her presence.

It was early in October when the prime bull moose passed near the two yearlings and, sensing the yearling female, drove Alces away. Once again he was alone, but there is never real loneliness in the wild. Winter would again bring companionship and spring would again be a period of discovery. Life moves, ever restless. Change is constant.

Five years have passed. Alces is a great prime bull, a monarch, crudely majestic, awkwardly graceful, deceptively fleet.

The bulls of the Upper Humber gather together in late

August. Jousting during early morning and evening throughout early September, they establish a breeding status in which yearlings are banished. The two-year-old bull ranks lowest of the mature animals. Among the older moose, the strongest and most formidable rank highest. Very old animals, like yearlings, wander alone.

Alces has antlers with twenty-four long points and wide palms spreading almost five feet from tip to tip. Rifles and snares have removed many of the bulls of this area and few rivals can challenge his supremacy.

As the bull groups wander, meeting others, the order is established over a wide area. Fights seldom occur. As bulls recognize one another, hesitant movements are followed by the identification of each relative position. Subtle differences in attitude will favour one male when bulls of nearly equal status meet. The fight will occur only when a wandering bull, a stranger to the territory, enters, or, rarely, when a bull does not accept his status.

The breeding order established, the bulls separate to begin a wandering search for females in their time. Challenging the small black spruce, they paw soil and swing their antlers. Some bulls dig at loose material and ground cover, baring the soil, then urinate in the earth, lie, and roll. Cows call the bulls as their time approaches.

Alces mates three times as his movements bring him into contact with cows in their time. He does not fight or even threaten rival males, for they sense his position among the animals of the herd.

In November, late, towards December, mating is over. Winter closes upon the wilderness. The moose is restricted in movement as deep, soft snow reaches high on the trunks of the fir.

Later, in January, Alces loses his great antlers. One at a time they drop, two days apart, as small trees bent easily by the antler pressure earlier in the winter now trip them from the growing pedicels of the skull.

Snow settles and travel is easier as winter progresses. In March, seven moose that have been together in a yard of aspen and fir separate. Alces travels in the direction of chainsaws, curious to learn what manner of beast speaks so tirelessly throughout the daylight hours. The woodsman provides food for moose and hare, who like the firs he cuts for pulp and, even more, the birch he cuts for firewood. The tops of both are left for the animals. Many years from now this area, cleared of commercial trees, will regenerate, producing much more food than the old forest.

Moose are less fearful of strangeness in the late winter and spring. Now Alces feeds near the working men as do other moose that have gathered to browse on the abundance of slash. And so the woodsmen set a snare of telephone wire and catch a cow by the neck. The struggle for life is violent and useless. Both the cow and the calf within her are dead when the men visit the snare. But the cow is bloated and declared unfit to eat, and is left.

Alces protects his growing antlers during the spring months. The blood supplying nourishment for the developing bone pulses through thick, velvet tissue. The growths are sensitive and injury means deformity. Avoiding thickets, Alces moves alone from bogs of new green towards the Humber backwater. Though the wilderness is his home, he ranges only a few miles in any one direction from the restricted range he knew as a calf. For months Alces inhabits one small part of his range, but he returns freely to all areas he has grown to know.

Woods roads in the spring are welcome areas where buds burst early and grass grows quickly because of the presence of light here which does not penetrate to the forest floor. But in midsummer these roads are no longer used as feeding lanes. They become a network of danger, criss-crossing the areas of movement for all moose and many other creatures of the wild.

As Alces walks into the open between the rows of trees, the truck lights stun him for an instant. He turns and runs, trotting down the centre, away. As he breaks into a gallop his speed decreases slightly. The men in the woods truck have not reckoned with the change of pace, nor a sudden switch in direction. There is no room to swerve.

BELETTE

The Weasel

The snow and the night have changed the face of the forest. Frothy white cones reach for the stars and the high, bright moon. Early that day the forest was green, but snow fell during the hours of light, stopping at dusk, and now the clear, white night is new.

In the dense fir, chickadees roost, brown caps and black caps together. Crossbills, jays, and grosbeaks sleep under the limbs and snow. In the morning, when the four-footed animals seek a sheltered rest, birds will emerge to greet the dawn and feed. If they slept till dawn was full and past, they would be safe from the predator, but this they cannot do.

A fox calls, his beautiful, mournful cry repeated. The dog seeks a mate this February night. As if in answer, the echo sounds. Then another fox takes up the cry and there are four.

Beside a fallen birch the snow stirs. It rises slightly a few inches on one side of the quilted log, and then the magic is repeated on the other side. Suddenly the snow explodes at the base of the upturned stump. A ghost-white Belette sits up, sniffing the frosted night. The moonlight, feeling its way between the giant boughs, picks out the black-bead eyes and, against the snow cushion, the black tip of a shivering tail. Belette moves into the beam of light and faces the moon. It is very bright to his eyes but he sits motionless for several minutes.

A great white owl sails over the tree-tips near by. It swoops into the forest and perches on a crooked, snow-covered crag of birch. The owl does not hear or see the weasel, for Belette has not moved. Once covered by the bird's shadow, he waits before making the movement that might reveal his presence to the ears and eyes of the owl.

Belette sits peering straight at the moon, paws slanting downwards against his stomach. Then, in one quick movement, he is hidden by snow-cover, silent and still beneath the blanket. The owl senses no movement. No sound is audible, even to the great drum ears inside the feathered head.

One of the foxes in the moonlight comes padding through the fluff. Beneath the owl tree he stops and looks up. He moves his head about, cocking it to one side, and sits down to examine the white bird outlined against the sky. Only the head of the owl moves to watch the fox. Vulpes frisks about, tired of watching. He dives into the snow, head first, front paws digging swiftly. Small snow-clouds flurry and settle in pieces on the tail and back of the fox. Vulpes looks up from his white cave towards the owl with a snow-covered face, and burrows again.

Belette must move now. The fox is very close. There is a purpose to the game. Quickly Belette slithers through the snow to the mouse-tunnels below and at once is gone. Vulpes digs, listens, smells, and digs. There is more than one odour here. The weasel has escaped, but where the weasel is there also may be mice.

Through the fluff to the old snow crust he digs – through the crust to the granules beneath. A movement under his paws stirs Vulpes to dig faster, leap high in the air – straight up, and down – then snap and drop the furry fluff. Vulpes holds his nose almost against the mouse, a paw resting at either side. The mouse sits up, pawing at the giant. Its teeth show and the mouth moves open and shut. Vulpes picks the mouse up gently. His lips are curled and only his incisors grip the prey. Snapping his neck back, he throws the mouse behind him into the fluffy snow. Quickly the fox jumps up, and down again at the mouse. The squeal is heard by the owl who swerves down from his perch, sailing close to Vulpes' back. The fox turns and snaps at the passing bird, looks down, and delicately chews off the digestive tract of his meal, to leave for the first morning jay.

Belette moves through the maze of tunnels, sometimes turning in his path to back-track a distance. Everywhere is the scent of mice. He crosses tiny midden heaps, fresh cut from rhizomes in the loose earth beneath the winter blanket. Mouse droppings are everywhere along the track-beaten maze. At a junction he surprises a resident moving across his path. The chase is short. Belette crunches the mouse's head, his needle teeth piercing the skull, and feeds.

It is late March. When the wind blows Belette's fur, brown shows beneath the white coat. Birds are becoming active, and the weasel, lying motionless beneath alder clumps, takes more of the flying creatures than during the time of winter's deadness.

April comes and Belette is greyish in colour, the brown hair casting shadows through the lingering white. Then May arrives and Belette is brown.

He travels farther now, even though food is plentiful. It is time to breed, and he seeks the sedentary female.

Gracilis moves out from her rock den high above the stream-bed. Over the clinging trunk roots turned quickly up by the sun and the earth, she moves over the ledge to the level ground above her. She is smaller by half than Belette. Narrower in the head and body, she is daintier, more fragile than the male, yet she disciplines her spring mate. For two weeks the weasels have shared the same den and the same food. Belette has brought small birds, beetles, and mice to the den. The animals chatter, purr, and sometimes bark. On occasion, Gracilis has found it necessary to nip Belette's ear to win her share.

Gracilis has hunted, too, but over a shorter distance and, over the days, with less success. Her needs are not as great as the male's. She is used to moving less, hunting less, eating less.

Now she moves beneath the fir stump on the ledge and out the opposite side, across the moss carpet to the big boulder, and is gone. Beneath this boulder is a den Gracilis has often known. The entrance is an opening in the moss carpet made by the near-surface root growth of a spruce tree, appearing only as a crack in the ground. Scurrying around through the fissures created by the struggling young soil over the boulder's edge, she searches for any living thing, for food. Now, out she pops and scurries outside the tree-cover into the young grass near the old abandoned camp. Soon, there will be a host of grasshoppers here, but now she passes through the grass to the camp and the many beetles.

Belette is stirred by his mate's return. The female acts differently. She shoves her head beneath Belette's and chuckles. Belette grasps the female's neck harshly, making Gracilis bark and screech. The mating begins. It is June the tenth.

The young will not be born until the following spring, for development of the now-fertile eggs will be retarded until late the following winter. The mating over, Belette will begin to stray farther from the female's home range until his movements bring him back infrequently. But in the spring, if he survives, he may return.

Mid-July finds the many young weasels born that spring exploring the outside world for the first time. Behind their mother they scamper over and under, searching out food. Throughout the summer and fall, many are caught by birds of prey and foxes. Some are drowned attempting to cross the too-swift streams. A few die from disease.

Belette seeks out the carrion and waste about the camp-grounds this summer. He feeds on discarded meat, taking fly and beetle larvae eagerly with the carrion. There are also plenty of grasshoppers and young birds, and Belette grows fat. In winter, exposure to the cold above snow-cover quickly destroys a weasel careless enough to rest outside. With fat and full stomach, the fall weasel is hardier than the late winter animal.

Weasels, too, can grow lazy. The easy life about the camp prompts Belette to go on living the same way. In September, when the wind ruffles his brown fur to show the approaching white coat beneath, Belette begins a journey to the farm.

By January the white hunter has destroyed all the rats and mice from the woodshed, but there is always garbage behind the building.

Today the smell of fresh meat lures Belette to the barn. Inside hang the dripping quarters of moose. On the floor the blood puddles emit a heavy odour. Belette darts straight to the warm liquid. There is movement near him but he is fearless. It is the cat who has been given credit for Belette's hunting successes, and now Belette himself is killed. It will be unfortunate for the cat if another weasel does not now arrive to do the feline's work for him.

Back in her rock den, Gracilis lies curled, a tiny ball of deadly life, her head hidden by a stomach and tail. Within her, six minute specks will become three male and three female weasels by spring, by the grace of many miracles.

VULPES

The Fox

All round the potato field above the brook the roots are piled high. Young cherry and birch grow from the topsoil in the debris and, with the roots and stumps, form a fence. Now the field is covered with hard-packed snow, granular beneath the morning crust. In the afternoon the crust melts and the prints of animals appear. Dog and cat have walked across this field. Other creatures with different prints pad the field at night on the frozen crust. Ice crystals reflect sunlight from the tracks of the nocturnal lynx and fox.

Deletrix is on the forest side of the fence moving towards her root-den. She carries a snowshoe rabbit, warm and limp. Its rear leg muscles jerk to answer impulses not yet dead. Within the natal den five yet-blind cubs lie together, fur balls apparently without noses and without ends to their tails. At the bitch fox's entrance, the balls will uncurl and the young will nurse as the mother feeds on the rabbit.

Yesterday there were six young. One, the smallest and weakest, Deletrix carried away and covered with sticks, abandoning it to death.

Gojavick, the male fox, is hunting. He has hunted food for the female for two weeks and is not now aware that his restless mate has left her cubs for a while. From now on she will hunt more.

Each day, as the snow melts, light increases within the

den. When the cubs are eighteen days old, tiny slits appear across their eyes. Three days later the slits see light and play begins.

Though the parents are careful in their approach to the birth chamber, they are seen. The farmer, who has lost a chicken, takes care to watch the back fields. With his son, he moves to dig out the young.

'You tink de bitch is in'er?' the son asks.

'I don't know, gimme dat pick and we'll soon find out if she's 'ere.'

The two men shovel and pick. The boy returns to the farm for a bar to pry rocks and an ax to chop roots.

'Wished we 'ad dynamite, skipper. A stick of dynamite 'ud do 'er.'

The older man nodded. 'We'll get 'em!' he said.

Deletrix watched from a distance of only a few yards. Gojavick was away hunting. He had returned to a small grass marsh for more meadow mice for the young. Yesterday he found several remaining from the winter's hardships and had brought three into the chamber.

Inside the den, the little foxes move towards the opening and the noise, hesitantly, then back away trembling. Their eyes and ears are alert. The smell is strange. But there is no one to guide them and they do not know what to do.

'What we gonna do wid 'em, skipper?'

'We'll club 'em and leave 'em and den watch an' de old lady'll be back sure and we'll shoot 'er.'

And they dig until the nest is bared and swing with shovel and pick at the kits and Deletrix moves. Like a flash she speeds between the killers, only a foot away from either. Her piercing shriek frightens the men who hesitate, too long, and one kit, Vulpes, escapes. The men move for their gun, but the bitch and her pup are away.

Vulpes travels with his mother all summer. He learns to hunt and meets often with Gojavick who carried food for him. It is a playful life for Vulpes, even without his brothers and sisters, for he plays with Deletrix the mother, with leaves and sticks, and most often with his own tail.

He likes to dig and push his nose into the soft earth as far as it will go, and he uses it to cover bones and debris. This is how Deletrix stores food, and Vulpes copies her.

Vulpes moves away from his mother and travels short distances by himself as the summer wanes. He spends many hours lying lazily in the sun, catching grasshoppers and young birds learning to fly. Late summer is a time of gradual parting for the bitch and her cub. November finds Deletrix far away from the farm area. Vulpes seldom sees her.

Winter brings hardship for all animals. Many will lose weight as the weather becomes cold. Vulpes has grown a heavy red coat to protect himself from the frost and when he wakens from his snow-bed the moisture clings, frozen to the tips of his guard-hair. The woolly under-fur of grey insulates his body and there is little loss of heat.

Foxes kill and steal to live, though most would rather steal. Vulpes hunts mice and plays with them after they are caught. When little birds come close the fox fools them by pretending he does not see them. Early in the winter Vulpes visits the farms and searches out the buildings carefully, but each visit makes him wilder and less bold.

His greatest thrill is chasing Lepus the hare. Lepus runs in great leaps and turns sharply to avoid being caught. To Lepus the chase means escape and life and he soars as if on wings above the branches normally passed under. Into the dense second-growth fir the hare glides, but he knows cover alone will not protect him from Vulpes the fox. One moment Vulpes is a calculating missile of the wilderness waiting to fire at a point he expects Lepus to pass. The next moment Vulpes is the orange flame streaking across the alder-bed and into the firs. Vulpes does not always catch the hare but this time he is successful, for the fir is not dense enough to prevent Vulpes' lightning-like movements close to the ground. If there were a few more inches of snow, the maze of lower branches would slow the fox's movements, or, if the fir growth were younger and bushier close to the snow line, perhaps the hare would live. Lepus screams as the fox grabs his back and holds for seconds before dropping him for a better grip at the base of the neck. Vulpes clamps the hare's neck strongly and throws the animal, with a snap of his head. Into the snow fluff the hare falls on its side. Lepus's hind legs move, but he has a broken neck and his final escape is death itself.

In February Vulpes sits one night in the light new snowfall. For many days he has felt restless, less inclined to hunt but more inclined to move. It is nearing mid-month. Vulpes cries out. He barks several times and then lies down, whimpers, and 'winds' the winter air with keen sense of smell. Far away on a distant knoll a second fox cries as if in answer. Mating time has arrived.

The nocturnal barking continues for several nights. Vulpes travels far during the dark hours and barks from several hills each night. During the day he sleeps.

It is mid-February when Vulpes finds his mate. She is a young animal, like Vulpes, and approaches her first breeding time. Together they travel across the frozen, moonlit crust, leaving prints side by side and overlapping in the hoarfrost – tracks that will be gone with the first tongues of sun.

The foxes mate five days after their meeting. They travel and hunt together and then go two miles away from their hunting-grounds to the great burned-over area blessed with hollow logs for foxes. They examine several den-sites before choosing a fallen forest monarch, hollow to the tip.

Vulpes is carrying sticks about in his mouth now and litters the log floor with his burdens. His mate moves less, mainly depending on the male to bring her food.

Fifty-one days from their time of mating, the bitch gives birth to six cubs. Two are grey-black and four are grey-yellow. As they grow, the two dark ones will become silver foxes. The yellowish ones will cover their wool with red-orange guard-hair. Vulpes hunts very hard for the bitch and the cubs. Rabbits have suddenly become scarce and he must take many small birds to augment the rabbit diet. There is much carrion in this country from the fall hunting season and the parts of carcasses left by poachers, but foxes are cautious of the dead.

Vulpes' nose, keen enough to discern bits of flesh beneath several feet of frozen snow, tells him of a dead animal not far from the den. Sitting on a stump a few feet from the den-entrance, he watches in the early morning. Ravens pick at a moose carcass recently bared as the snow melted. The object was seen by the carrion-feeders from the great dead trees, spires of the clearing, and now they feed. The birds stay with the carcass for two or three days and then Vulpes investigates, only to find the rib-cage on the top picked white and clean. Beneath, the ribs still lie partly frozen and the ravens and crows have worked with less success. It is midnight and the moon outlines the little dog, tail humped, scratching, biting, and tearing to loosen the meat bones from the partly frozen earth. He is successful and the cubs will eat.

In May the bitch moves her cubs to another den-site. Now the young play about the entrance and sometimes move away. Each strange object is a lesson in caution and the cubs learn quickly.

Vulpes pays less attention to his family as they grow older, though he constantly returns to visit or bring some new-found carrion, or a rabbit. He hunts alone at night, returning to his former haunts, shying away from man or his tracks, jumping high over trails where man has passed.

At night he sits on the edge of a log watching the shadowy moose walk across the open. A faint, low howl begins, repeating itself, higher and louder, and suddenly ends. It is the lynx, Cervier, calling from the forest on the other side of the bog marsh. Vulpes does not move. Though lynx and fox compete for the same foods, they are not enemies. Many times Vulpes has been close to the lynx, though the cat has not been aware of the dog's presence. Vulpes' nose is sharp. Cervier's sight is keen but his nose is dull. The lynx cry does not arouse Vulpes' curiosity. He is indifferent. Yet at the second cry he stands, slowly turns, and trots away, then stops and barks a shivering cry as if to answer Cervier before he sinks into the forest.

September is a wonderful time of the year to Vulpes. Nights are cool and his new growing coat protects him during the chilly hours. A month ago he was a woolly, ragged creature looking gaunt and thin. Now he is a new fox. This is the time of year for berries. Since August he has fed on raspberries and partridge berries as well. Marsh cranberries hold on even until spring and now sprinkle the bogs with tiny red-pepper dots. Vulpes feeds and fattens. A fox adds to his meat diet anything that he can find. In the spring, grasses are good. In the summer, insects; and in the fall, berries. So now he travels to the barrens above the timber slopes.

Vulpes sits on a brown rock in the middle of the clearing. It is early morning and blueberries that grow in abundance in the acid sub-soil fill the fox's belly to roundness. A moose appears and Vulpes crouches low. He does not fear the moose and when his nose has determined there is no alien smell he will sit up again. Soon a second moose, a third, and a fourth appear. They are bulls and they gather for a purpose. A great large male with giant antlers approaches. This is Alces. Each animal challenges the huge bull. Antlers are placed together and each strives to shove the other backwards. The half-ton creatures snort heavily and cough as they strain to force Alces back. Four try and fail. As each animal tries, the others watch. At first curious, then eager to join the fight, Vulpes jumps to the ground and prances toward Alces. The giant moose eyes the dog fox and waves his mighty antlers at the dodging fur menace. Vulpes squeals with pleasure and challenges again.

He dodges gracefully away at each swerve of Alces' antlers. Suddenly he is attacked from behind as a shadow closes over him. A second bull wishes to strike at the little dancing dog. Vulpes dashes quickly out of the great deer circle and cautiously creeps around them, eyeing the group with short, sweeping glances, yet unconcernedly. The bulls watch the fox until their dim eyesight can no longer discern movement.

Man is everywhere in the wind some days. Vulpes travels farther into the forests to avoid him. Deletrix has returned to man to steal. This has been her life and becomes the cause of her death.

In the next green spring the great log contains six kits. Two are dark. Four are light. The bitch nurses the young. Vulpes hunts again for his mate.

Interlude

MARTES

The Marten

Martes, son of Abidish, bounds across the green-ferned forest floor, silent pads crinkling the cushion mosses. He moves to the alders lining a creek where Lepus feeds at night.

Long long ago, before Lepus existed, the forests, greater then, held Arcticus the giant hare, Obseet the bird, and Souris the mouse. Martes preyed upon all these, on the insects, on Ondra the muskrat, and often on the eggs of Lagopus the white partridge nesting in the heath at the barren's edge. When animals died in their wild homes, Martes fed upon their bodies, driving away his tiny cousin Belette but not Cervier the lynx or Vulpes the fox. Great black carrion birds, flapping their wide, worn wings, opened their bills and crackled. Martes had no fear and sometimes killed the carrion bird to feed upon fresh blood and meat. Here he fared ahead of all the competitors and at such times he would leave them a rotting carcass, content – his belly bulging hard with bird.

And so it was that Martes entered upon the scene and watched as the mighty bitch bear cuffed life from her helpless cub when the offspring could not follow. The giant steel trap had been torn from the log drag by the female but she could not loose its grip from the swollen paw of the young. Tremors of the young life entering death rippled the sticks placed upon the cub by the mother and, when she had covered it all, she was gone, and Martes came and fed.

Today the giant forests have melted away. The marten home has been reduced. In the Beothuck's time there was much room to live. Then the Micmac came and warred with his brother, and the forests caught fire and burned. The fishermen destroyed coastline trees, cutting and burning, and they penetrated interior woodland to cut the majestic pine for ships. But the greatest destruction of the forests is still taking place, for the woodcutters' age began late in Newfoundland.

Abidish was destroyed too, with deadfall and snare. White trappers captured him with four nails driven downwards into a tiny tree cavity before the bait. Abidish reached in but could not get out. And though it became illegal to capture marten or sell the marten pelt, killing continued.

In the virgin forest and about its edges Martes has no enemy except man. The fox cannot climb for him, the lynx is not agile enough to catch him. Birds of prey are few and ill prepared to capture Martes. Few marten become prey for their forest neighbours.

Martes leaves the bear cub. He has fed upon the lips and cheeks and jowls, tearing the woolly fur away from skin. About the face he has been able to grasp solidly and worry the tender meat beneath the skin. It takes almost an hour for Martes to eat his fill, and his departure, following many false starts, is a reluctant one.

Humping over hillock and rock, the velvet creature moves on and on, over streams and along banks. Into holes, cracks, and crevices the tiny nose runs, alerted to smells of food and female. Martes moves about his home, ever active, never halting as breeding nears. He seeks the sleek, small female who lives in the rock-crevice by the waterfall, and finds her.

And what does man know of Martes?

'In 1935 me and George Hunt got eleven marten cats in Birchy country but when we went back in de spring two fellers from Howley 'ad been in and covered de country.

My son, I don't believe dey left a marten cat in de whole place.

'Course, dere's still lots of marten cats down Grand Lake and on Glovers' Island. Dey sees 'em all around de camps on Little Grand and all over de place. Must be hundreds of 'em left dere. And I hear tell dat over Gander way and somewhere 'round Bishops dere's marten cats. And I tink dere's sposed to be some up Silver Mountain country and here and dere all over.

'What? No, I ain't seen one since about 1938 except on de Labrador.'

Martes and his mate travel together along the stream's edge. They seek out the mouse among the rocks and grass, and climb the mountain ash or dogberry to eat its fruits. Through the timber of the hill-side and out on to the heath threaded with the paths of caribou they bound. Blueberries and hare are here but they go onwards into the grassy plains. Martes seldom travels into the barren country except in the spring when the ptarmigan nests. Sometimes he ranges here when food is scarce, but this is not the cause of his movement now. It is the female, who will soon be ready to mate. She will wait until the following spring to bear her young.

Vulpes pretends he does not notice the strange creatures that look almost like foxes. He watches them come over the rise and onto the grass marsh where he hunts. Crouching low, hugging the ground, Vulpes peeks above the waving bulrush, his nose alert for scent. The marten bounds within fifty feet before he smells the fox. Then suddenly he turns and lopes away with his mate. No sound emitted, no sign shown. Martes and his mate disappear into the shrubs at the edge of the marsh.

Vulpes is not idle. Are these animals playful? His lightning movement has only barely failed to allow him to catch the marten on the bog and he enters the dense interlocked stem jungle. Around corners and down corridors Vulpes streaks on the marten's trail. He short-cuts but guesses wrong, then right, and, as the martens emerge along a hare path into the tiny open spot where Vulpes waits, the fox is undecided. Should he play? His indecision allows the frightened creatures to enter cover again. Their very presence is a problem to the fox. Vulpes turns and his orange flame penetrates the tiny jungle once again. This is excitement. The chase fills the fox. This is his life and joy.

Martes cannot run fast much longer. He searches for trees, running, back-tracking, circling. His mate, very close, follows Martes' movements. The three animals break onto the moss-covered boulders at once. Martes leaps and catches the balsam limb that leads to safety. The female misses the branch and Vulpes reaches and snaps, a turmoil of teeth and legs, chatter and shriek. Between the fox's hind legs the female goes. She circles and leaps again for the branch, catches it and scrambles to safety.

Vulpes lies down, panting atop the cool boulder. He laps his leg where the marten's teeth have pricked. Vulpes rests and watches and waits.

And what does man know of Martes?

'When was de last time I seen a marten cat? Hell, dere's lots of 'em 'round Grand Lake. Yes sir, right here right around de camp. Why, I know two fellers from St. Georges been trappin' 'em every winter right up to about 1955, or so. Oh, dere's marten cats around all right. I don't know 'bout anywheres else but dey're here.

'Down north where I comed from we called 'em wood cats, but dey're all the same. I don't know's dere's any left down dere, but here, why, hell, I seen four, five tracks right at dis here camp last winter. Dey comes in around here and feeds on garbage.'

Vulpes stretched. He had watched the marten for several minutes but now he was anxious to move on. His curiosity was not strong enough to keep him, and the mice were plentiful through the shrub growth in the marsh. He stopped and turned to watch the marten lying motionless in the tree, and he cocked his head. Then, indecision gone, he trotted off and did not look back.

Martes did not leave the tree until night. When darkness quilted the forest edge, he drifted gracefully to the ground and bounded away down the hill. The female followed.

When they reached the great forest growth the velvet creatures chose a giant tree and climbed to its highest limbs beneath the moon and stars and stayed till the sky lightened.

RANGIFER

The Caribou

Each April there is one day in the northern forests unmistakably different from all the days before. It is that day when the fading winter draughts are first joined by the warmer gusts that herald the return of spring.

This one day always arrives during a period of bright, sunny daylight, glistening, ice-covered snow, and cloudless, frosty darkness. It is a period of orientation for all mammal life and all bird life. This day signifies the end of the cold, still, heavy days of winter and the beginning of the revival of life.

There had been a week of bright, sunny, cold days in this April 1960. The woodland was crusted, even in the most dense cover – crusted so firmly the sharp-hoofed moose could tread without breaking through. At night the frost-crystals would settle to the solid surfaces of the land and forest, so that at each sunrise the world of white was softly blanketed with a new, clean smoothness, and the animals that moved during the early-morning hours left their almost invisible prints behind them.

On the high, barren, snow-blown slopes of Mount St. Gregory, the blue snow-ice glistened in the sunlight. In some places it reflected starlight, and the moon's rays danced crazily from its slanting, uneven ridges. During the early darkness of these days, an accompanying wonderment of skylight, the dancing curtains, framed this mountain with wavering sheets of brightness meeting at the top, the centre of all the sparkling universe, in a rounded ball of glistening red and yellow.

On the plateau itself, stretching along North Arm on the south, bordering the evergreen forest on the east and the Trout River Ponds to the north, ice covered the slopes below the naked ridge-tops and above the snow-crusted flats of the valleys. And in these valleys, the valleys of Liverpool and Crabbs Brook, only trickles of water moved, for the frost had eaten the moisture this winter and pushed to the base rock over all the plateau and the mountain. It was a time of quiet life, past the dreaded winter's deadness and yet too early for the gushers of water to be brought by the coming spring.

At this time of the year the Gregory caribou herd always became restless. Within weeks, now, the doe must be on her fawning grounds, many miles from this wind-swept mountain country. For centuries the round-hoofed, grey-coated spring animals had moved down the rocky cliffs from the plateau to the forest and travelled north across the Governors Pond woodland lichen country, through the timber, and on to the great chain of hills leading north on the peninsula. There, the does made their way to the yellow bogs and gave birth while the stags wandered about singly or in small companies, living slowly, moving little, putting on fat.

The caribou had always lived on the Gregory Plateau for part of the year. They moved onto the highland area at the first snowfall of autumn and ate the lichens on the great mountain slopes and the slopes overlooking Chimney Cove, the Gregory River, and the Trout River Ponds. In stormy weather they moved into the valleys of the brooks and fed on the tree lichens that grew in abundance from the spruce. If the storms were prolonged and the winds westerly, the animals sometimes moved into the forest below the great rock cliff-borders of the plateau. This country was rich in lichens on the ground and on the spruce and larch trees, present in park-like stands over the knolls of the greater valley. Then, some time in late April, the animals trekked north, away from the plateau to the northern hills. It was on this trek and in those hills that they sometimes mingled with other herds of caribou from the Humber Valley, the Topsail barrens, and the Hinds plains. Some years, the Gregory herd would be increased by wanderers from other herds and some years it would be decreased when a few of its own body would stray to other groups and move away to a different country. These stragglers were often young, anxious, adventurous stags, in search of does.

It was April the tenth, 1960, when Rangifer felt the first warm draughts, mixed with the clinging cold of the waning winter. During the past few days he had been feeding upon tree lichens in the valley of Crabbs Brook. All his life he had fed on the lichens hanging from the slow-grown spruce and fir in this valley. He liked both the black lichens and the yellow-green ones. They were good for him during the late winter and early spring and he sought them out instinctively.

This day, Rangifer moved slowly over the blue ice, his broad, round hoofs making sure of safe footing on the glazed and glassy surface. He headed for the lichen stands; ground cover in the area of dense heath, which stayed blown clear most years because of its position on the hanging western abutments of Mount St. Gregory. Reflected from the blue surface, the sun's heat made the densely coated animal slacken his pace, and sometimes pause. He passed the boulder garden about the peak, still stopping occasionally, and settled after a moment's hesitation on a protected spot at the end of a small, yellow marsh. He was no longer interested in his destination, and he lay facing the breezes, his front legs tucked in under him. The tops of the yellowed, old-year, grass-like bulrush waved from the light, unsettled snow cover, outlining the shape of the marsh he was in.

The woodland caribou lives alone with his kind, apart from all other mammal life. His home is sometimes wind-swept, rock-spotted, and barren, or it may be protected, level, parkland cover. The caribou lives by movement – wild and independent. His movements are directed by weather and by his changing seasonal requirements for foods that grow in particular sites.

The movement from behind the boulder was slight. The man stepped into the open and stood motionless. Rangifer, facing away into the wind, did not move. His senses told him nothing of what might be behind. He lived facing the wind, depending on his sense of smell to keep him from danger.

Rangifer heard the shot and trembled more from the impact of the bullet than from fright. Slowly, he worked his knees to withstand his body's weight and pushed himself up, hind quarters first. Turning, he saw the man, blurred to him, fifty yards away. The man was standing quietly, watching his target. There was, he knew, no need to fire again. The caribou moved slowly towards the danger as if trying to distinguish this new strangeness. Closer, slowly closer, his great bulk moved. He coughed, and bright red blood spattered the snow-sheet before him. Close enough now to detect the odour, even against the wind, Rangifer gradually settled down, to rest. This was the end of Rangifer's life, which had begun almost four years before.

Rangifer was born on May the twenty-fourth, 1956. His mother, Tarandus, had chosen the edge of an open bog near a tiny clump of black spruce growing from a dry, four-inch mat of yellow-grey lichens. She had carried him for 227 days from the day of conception the preceding October.

He was a perfect offspring and stood shakily four hours after birth to feed. Tarandus had cleansed him dry right after birth. He was a light, reddish brown, almost tan, with a dark, brown-black muzzle. All little caribou look the same, but each is very special to the mother animal.

The first day, Tarandus stayed with her offspring, except for quick, casual trips of a few yards for water and green food. Towards the evening of the second day she nuzzled him to accompany her about the open marsh. They moved slowly northward towards the great grassy marshes at the head-waters in Crabbs Brook Valley, two miles away. Sometimes Rangifer would frisk ahead of his mother as she stopped to feed. Often he nursed hungrily. Soon his mother would feel the energy drain and feed more herself.

By dark they were standing alone on a tiny peninsula stretching into a shallow steady in the brook. Here they lay down. Twice during the night they moved together about the marsh for an hour or more as Tarandus fed. For the rest of the night they slept, and daylight found them standing in the great marsh, Tarandus feeding upon the tender green shoots of early spring while Rangifer nursed.

It was long after daylight when Rangifer detected the presence of the other caribou. Tarandus had known – had expected them to be here, on this day, at this time. She had lived for seven years now, and for the past five years she had produced young on the same fawning ground. She had moved here instinctively the first year, immediately after the birth. The other does and their fawns were here then, and they had always been here since. This year's lapse of time, staying alone with her offspring, was unusual. Sometimes a few days would elapse before they would all be together, but gather they must, and did.

One day, eons of time before Tarandus, a group of twenty doe caribou had gathered together with their helpless fawns by sheer accident, after fighting off three wolves. Throughout the years, other events like this had occurred and the protective habit persisted. Now there are no wolves and few bears here, but the pattern remains, perhaps for future needs.

There were fifteen other does and nine fawns on the great

yellow marsh five days later. The fawns were all light brown with dark muzzles. The does were a shabby grey-white in their winter's garment. After the early-morning feeding, the does would gradually bed down to cud while their offspring slept or rested beside them. Soon after noon, the first doe would stand and begin to graze. By mid-afternoon all the herd would be feeding, the fawns frisking about the mothers and the barren does. These 'dry' does took considerable interest in all the offspring of the herd.

Rangifer played all afternoon with the other fawns, feeding at intervals. Sometimes another fawn would try to nurse with Rangifer, but Rangifer balked at this attempt at sharing, so that the visitor would usually stand at a safe distance and watch after a few short challenges from Rangifer. If the other fawn persisted, the victimized cow would strike at the intruder with forefeet or charge threateningly.

One day, when Rangifer was four weeks old, a near-by female fawn became sick. Instead of playing actively, she held her head to one side, staggered when trying to stand, and refused nourishment. Her condition became worse the next day, and on the third day a great hole appeared in the side of her neck. White, pasty fluid drained from the opening. The fawn could no longer stand after the hole appeared and the doe seldom moved more than twenty or thirty feet away. The emaciated animal died where she lay. For several days the mother remained near by, until one day she moved out among the other animals, mothering fawns that stood alone. She continued to travel with the group until it began to disintegrate, in early July. After the death of this first fawn, most of the others fell ill. Only Rangifer and one other were spared. By early July, five of the original ten fawns had died. The other three, which were also afflicted, had recovered. Some of the illnesses had come as a result of an attack by lynx, which seldom killed but often injured. And through these injuries, where the sharp canine teeth had penetrated, bacteria entered the blood stream of the hapless calves. Yet causes of the sickness in some remain a mystery to man even today.

Throughout the summer months, Rangifer often saw one or more of his early playmates. Sometimes several caribou would be together and sometimes Rangifer and Tarandus would be alone for days. He fed considerably on grasses and sedges after the first of July, and by September he spent as much time grazing and browsing as his mother did, though he still nursed when Tarandus let him.

September found the whole caribou herd on the great North Arm barrens. There were four small groups totalling thirty-five animals. Rangifer and Tarandus were with seven other caribou. One great stag dominated the group, and although he never chased Rangifer he often threatened the medium-sized stag and the small yearling stag, known to men as a 'pricket' stag. Three old does and a yearling pricket doe were also in the group. Rangifer paid little attention to this gathering of animals, though he felt less closely attached to his mother than he had during the warm weeks of the past summer.

Within this harem unit no one challenged the great stag's supremacy, but once, in mid-September, a stag from another group came very close. The great stag moved towards the intruder, head down and slowly waving from side to side. The intruding stag, at least as big as the Great One, met the challenge and the two placed their antlers together. Suddenly they tensed, muscles rippling and bulging. Each strained to shove the other backwards. The great stag slowly inched ahead as the intruder weakened. Then, in an instant, the intruder was pushed back and stumbled. As his side struck the ground with a thud, he struggled away from the victor. The great stag stood menacingly above, staring and moving his head but making no attempt this time to gore the helpless, defeated animal. Thoroughly beaten, the intruder made his way towards the group from which he had come.

The does and prickets in Rangifer's group had watched the battle intently. The whole affair took about three minutes, yet the defeat was complete and the stags so near exhaustion that the Great One gasped for breath and his sides swelled and shrank deeply for minutes after. This was Rangifer's first experience of fighting among his own kind. He would live to see several more battles and to take part himself.

On October the first, the four groups joined on the eastern end of the North Arm barrens not far from the tinkling headwaters of Liverpool Brook. For four days the largest of the stags asserted their supremacy by chasing younger males and occasionally challenging each other. There were only two exceptionally large stags, the Great One and the animal he had already defeated, but three others were large enough to assert themselves successfully, so that the herd had five master stags.

The herd remained as one unit, except for the loss of does after conception, for three weeks. Master stags battled furiously on occasions, but the younger males moved away from slight, intimidating advances made by the older ones. Sometimes an old stag, like the Great One, would stand 'bushgazing', motionless for an hour or more, staring in one directtion, his neck bent slightly downwards.

On October the eleventh, the first mating occurred. Tarandus had reached her time, and the Great One sought her out. Two other does also conceived on this day, and mating continued until the last doe was bred on October the seventeenth.

Three days after Tarandus had conceived, she moved away, followed by Rangifer. The other two does that had conceived at the same time as Tarandus also left. And so, after each female mated, the group shrank, until by October the eighteenth only the yearlings, stags, and barren does remained.

Slowly the group disintegrated, and a ragged exodus began as the animals moved along the barrens towards the head-waters in the brook valleys. Here in the wide basin at the head of Crabbs Brook was the pass in the hills, no longer used by the animals. At one time great numbers of caribou filed between these hills where the settlers from Trout River met the animals, and killed them. Today, the deer stayed in the valleys or moved aimlessly back across the barrens.

During the post-breeding restlessness four hunters climbed the bluffs from North Arm and searched the barrens for ptarmigan and hare. They knew the Gregory Plateau well and had hunted here all their lives. Hunting without dogs, they killed a great many ptarmigan and a few hares, and each man killed a caribou, though for over twenty years caribou-shooting had been prohibited here.

After a long midwinter, spent in the great lowland country about Governors Pond, on the barrens, and on Mount St. Gregory, the month of March found the caribou moving aimlessly once again over the snow-crust. And March also brought the settlers up from Chimney Cove to kill their annual caribou. There were six families living in Chimney Cove now, and ten men represented these families on the slopes of the windswept mountain. They killed ten caribou, grouped as they stood. Twenty-one animals remained on the plateau, nineteen fewer than there had been after fawning a year before.

Now the old men can tell us a part of the story, though they sometimes err in their beliefs of what exists today.

'We used to kill caribou and taste the wolf on 'em. They was run ragged over from the Table Lands, down across the pond, up the gulch and over to the mountain and back again. Two, three times they'd go maybe, but the wolf 'ud get the deer every time.

'I know, I seen 'em do it. Why, one morning I was goin'

down the ice hopin' to get a deer at the head of the gulch or in the pass when I come across the tracks. They was blood there then, where the wolf was nippin' the hocks of the deer. They was headed east up to the Table Lands. Then, just after I passed the tracks, I heard something coming, and, sure 'nuff, back a me and a-comin' down off the Table Mountain was a deer and on his heels was the wolf! They was too far to shoot so after they'd gone up the west side, slippin' and slidin' and fallin', I went back a couple a hundred yards and waited.

'Wull, it warn't long, maybe twenty minutes or a half hour, when back they come, right down towards me, and when they hit the ice the deer went down. The wolf jumped in and back out and slashed at the deer's hind quarters and legs and got 'im hamstrung complete. I rushed over and shot 'em both. They never knowed I was there.

'Wull, sir, I packed out two quarters and the hide on me hand-sled but never went back after the rest. You could taste the wolf on 'im easy enough!

'Nowadays the deer has gone altogether. Warn't more'n twenty year past I killed the last 'un right out there on the pond ice. There ain't no more now. Least, I never seen none the past twenty year and I don't believe anyone else has either. 'Course, could be the deer don't use this side of Crow Head no more and maybe if they's still there, they stays in one place.

'We used to depend on deer here all right. Every spring in March month we'd git deer, all we wanted right handy. Some fellers went down the coast and up. I know old Jobie used to go in the country from Sally's Cove with komatik and team and he'd bring out six, seven deer to once. Sometimes them fellas 'ud go in and kill the deer in early winter then go back in March and bring 'em out. And sometimes they'd run into more deer on the way fer the meat and leave the cached meat where't lay. Fergit altogether 'cause was easier killin' again.

'Times was once when some of the boys down the coast used to go in and kill twenty, thirty deer just fer a fry of tongues.

'The deer are all gone now, boy! They don't come 'round here no more. All moved back into the country. Must be thousands back in the country, though. Least, there used to be thousands right down here. Why, I seen deer right there next my barn in the spring of the year. They was all over the Table Mountain and down Indian Head and up Crow Head.

'No more wolves, neither. Fact is, I killed the last wolf right there on the river back of the mill about forty, fifty years ago. Must of been about 1910 or thereabouts. Always figgered there must be lots of wolves, but we never seen one after that.'

Rangifer was one year old in June 1957. Fleet afoot, deep-chested and strong, the yearling caribou was the animal most sought after by meat-hunters in years past. The first antler growth was apparent now. Velvet spikes and brow stood from the bony knobs on Rangifer's head.

No longer with his mother who had long since deserted him to calve, Rangifer roamed with a large stag, the Great One, over the plateau and the flat Governors Pond woodland-lichen country. Now, after the winter's diet of tree lichens and ground lichens, the caribou fed lavishly on the green shoots of wild grasses, sedges, and rushes. When the ice covered their feeding-grounds on the heights, the caribou had moved to the valley and were forced to dig through many feet of snow to obtain their lichen diet. Sometimes they fed on the buds and bark of larch and from the hanging festoons of tree lichens on the larch and spruce. Now they would vary their diet and, through the summer and fall, add many items to it. In all, the deer would feed upon forty or more species of fungi, lichens, and herbaceous and woody plants through the year.

One morning, as Rangifer lay on a rock outcrop overlooking a small pond, he noticed a movement strange to him. Turning, he watched the Great One who lay near by, looking for a sign he might follow. The Great One saw the movement, too, but paid it little heed. He had often watched the moose feeding during the summers past.

The moose fed on grasses and rushes at the edge of the pond. He, too, was taking on a new diet from his winter's woody twigs. The greens in the marshes would be added to as the summer progressed. Later, he would feed on aquatic plants, and all through the summer he would seek out the young leaves of birch and willow.

As the huge beast moved about the edge of the pond closer to Rangifer, the pricket stag grew excited. The moose was a large bull. Its velveted antlers were still small but the bulk of the animal more than doubled Rangifer's. In a short while the moose was abreast of the young deer, and, catching scent of another animal, it turned. From twenty feet they watched each other. Rangifer lay with his front legs under him, bent at the knees. His hind legs were drawn up close, so that with only a slight roll of his weight they would be under him and he would be bounding away, head and tail held high. But the pricket stag was curious too, and so he lay watching, smelling, listening intently, ready to move but waiting for a sign from the moose or the great stag. No sign was given. After a moment's examination of the smaller animal, the moose continued his feeding, moving steadily along the pond's edge. Rangifer watched until the animal drifted into cover minutes later.

Now a biologist studies the caribou – too late.

'I first saw the animals from the helicopter in July. We set up camp and worked over the herd for sex and age ratios for three weeks. The range is adequate and I think the herd could continue as it is or maybe increase with protection, barring heavy losses from this crazy disease we're trying to fathom.

'We caught two men from a woods camp with two animals which they claimed to have killed for camp meat. This is what the mining-camp foreman used to do before the herd was reduced, I guess. The men were charged, found guilty, and let off with suspended sentences. This isn't good enough, and as far as I'm concerned the animals are finished now. They are too far removed from people to create any political interest and I've been ordered to work on the big interior herds and those small ones closer to town.'

Rangifer moved with the Great One even after the large animal turned on him several times during September. During this month they sought out Tarandus and her spring fawn and another doe and her fawn. These does were with the Great One in his harem of past years, and the Great One was Rangifer's father and the father of all Tarandus' offspring.

All the stags now wore their clean white neck manes over swollen muscles. Their contrasting white and brown separated them from the duller, grey-brown does – drab beside the noble male animals. This year, Rangifer was chased often, not only by the Great One but by the other stags, larger than he was.

The breeding took place as always, and after the month's activity Rangifer moved about with the Great One again. They were together all winter and throughout the month of March when the Chimney Cove hunters returned and took seven of the remaining animals, as many as had been born that year.

There had been no sickness last spring but nine does had been killed, and before the fawning season of 1958 only nineteen caribou remained in the Gregory herd.

And what is the attitude of the woods contractor who, perhaps unknowingly, has the power to maintain this herd and others like it?

'When we first opened the road into Taylors Brook, there were hundreds of caribou all around the camps. We killed one each during the season in 1949 and again in 1950. Then, in 1951, we had to move up to the Neds Steady Crossing and were lucky enough to get a few. The next year no caribou crossed there at all. They just went.

'Oh, they're still in the valley, all right. They moves down on the Great Northern Peninsula, you know. Thousands of them down there. I've heard tell of men seein' herds of two, three hundred when they was in furrin' back of Silver Mountain.

'Now we moved up here by Governors Pond and I'm damned if there ain't a whack of deer right behind us on that plateau there. Why, last year, two of the boys went up there and killed two in the summer. 'Course, they got caught, but it was only an accident that the warden happened along and then they got off anyway.

'So, now we got this here fawn we picked up. Took six of us to corner him. Boy, could he run! But we got 'im and we're feeding him milk. Boys sure like him around the camp, you know. Makes a great pet.

'What's that, cook? What? Where is he? What's the matter with him? Dead? Well, I'll be damned! Look here, the damned deer died on us.'

Five fawns had been born this season and one was caught and carried away by woodsmen. Then, in the fall, hunters from the woods camp came onto the plateau again. The contractor led his men to the breeding herd and they killed twelve deer. Tarandus and her last fawn were killed.

Rangifer roamed the country with the Great One during the winter. They no longer travelled down into the flat Governors Pond lichen country.

In January there was a great storm. The caribou grew restless and milled about for two days in the blizzard. On the third day, the Great One disappeared as he walked beside Rangifer. He had stumbled over the ledge and fallen into North Arm. This left ten deer to perpetuate the herd.

When spring came once more to the tiny group of deer, two fawns were born. One doe, a barren animal, was without antlers, but the does with fawns had carried their antlers until the fawns were dropped. A fourth doe had borne no fawn because she was sickly. The four does were all that was left of the once-great fawning herd that had in years past travelled fifty miles or more to the endless grassy leads on the western end of the Great Northern Peninsula to drop their young.

As they had always done, the does kept with their fawns throughout the summer. They watched the female bear and her cubs feeding on old-year berries and new-year grasses. They knew where the geese nested and reared their young. They watched the white-headed eagles soar over the bluffs along the Gulf of St. Lawrence.

Frisking over the marshes like wind-blown leaves, the caribou fawns lived their young lives as hundreds of others had done in this herd before them, and just as Rangifer had done.

Once, in late summer, Rangifer and the barren doe, who were travelling together, watched the fox catch a moulting duck along the edge of a marshy pond. Life was complete in the deer world for those who remained, even to the nose bots which had so pestered Rangifer since his first year. There was no warning to the individual caribou that the end was near. The fawns of this spring did not know they were the last.

In October, Rangifer fought. Two other stags remained besides Rangifer. He defeated them both. One was too aged, the other too weak to stand against the powerful thrusts of the beautiful young stag. Rangifer was master of the herd, a group of twelve, including two male fawns.

And so the mating season came upon them. Rangifer mated

two does. Another doe, the one that had been ill, now was sickly and thin, so she took no part in the breeding activities. Rangifer was the master stag when only three years and four months old.

Soon after the rut and breeding was finished, the hunters came from the woods camp. The contractor and his men shot and killed eleven caribou, including the emaciated doe, which was left along with the aged stag to rot on the mountain slopes.

BEOTH

The Wolf

It was the wind that spoke. At first the voice was distant, un-
clear. The words were muffled as if the frosted branches of
the dense fir forest were blotting out what I strained to hear.
I moved outside my tent and stood over the staccato fire that
boiled the kettle, and listened. Perhaps I had been wrong and
had heard no voice at all. No, the murmur was there, tremu-
lous, whispering now stronger, now fading. If only the
branches did not crack and rattle so! There now, a word
spoken clearly. It came not only from windward but from
all the forest. 'Wolf'. Certainly it was meant for me.

Many times during the past few winters I had heard of a
wolf from the north or from the south or east or west. I had
myself seen a track, though it certainly could not have been,
for wolves no longer exist in Newfoundland. Yet today again
I saw the track, bold, in fresh snow atop the crust, and I followed it. Through stunted fir, across marshes, out of my way
I followed it, determined to see, to find the source of the
pads upon the snow.

In mid-afternoon I found the kill. A moose calf, emaciated
from some sickness or abnormality, had this January day
fallen victim, perhaps for the good of its kind. The hocks
were sliced, the throat was torn and the beast's eyes bulged
in death, the terror of the attack increased by the presence of
the predator so many years extinct.

Extinct? How could this be? I left the animal, still warm with clotted blood frosting over the portions from which great jaws had torn flesh, and followed until dark overcame me in this small valley among the Hobblies. I made camp under the firs, though the tracks continued.

Now the wind whispered clearly, 'Wolf – wolf – wolf.' I felt no fear, but I could not speak, nor did I feel the need. Alone, I stood attentive to the wind.

'Cold light shone one night many years ago on the barren mountain you know as Soldiers Hill. Mist rose, as clouds, from ponds dotting the sloping plateau toward the east, then moved slowly, white billows, soldiers of the moon god. Effortlessly, to and fro, about the treeless plains they moved.

'In the valleys below the slopes no light shone. The moon was not high enough in its majesty to penetrate all this living world, and dead.

'On the mountainside dotted with boulders gleaming from cold crystals, once molten, a life lay quiet, motionless as the rocks themselves. This was Beoth, wolf-son of Lupus. Somewhere in the vastness of the night Lupus was cutting and tearing the shank of a caribou killed during the early morning of that same day. She would bring the shank to her offspring.

'Beoth sat up. He had waited long, and impatience is strong in the young. As he sat up, there suddenly lay before him a great black wolf, much larger than Beoth or Lupus or any other. Beoth stood and, as he did so, the black wolf grew larger. Quickly Beoth jumped behind a boulder. The black wolf appeared beside him, covering, blotting out, the stone of refuge.

'Beoth ran down the slope, thunder beating within his ears. The black wolf matched his leaps, always beside him. Then, suddenly, into the darkened vale the tormentor was gone. Beoth, alone again, learned then that his world was darkness. To the wolf, light is fear, night is peace. Beoth waited for his mother.

'Beoth grew until he was the largest of the remaining wolves, those that had not fallen prey to traps of steel, snares of wire, or lead from guns. With his mother and a wolf family from far to the north he hunted the caribou, following the animals to their breeding-grounds, their wintering yards, north in the late winter with the great migration and back again in the fall. On the spring calving-grounds the wolves fared best. Though the does gathered together with their fawns for protection, there was seldom need to attack the healthy. There were often sick ones or weak ones the herd would be better off without. Indeed, the wolves' attacks saved many caribou lives, because the disease could not spread when the sick ones were removed from the living group at the first sign of weakness.

'So, too, many years before, the wolf had been friend to the Indian for whom Beoth was named. Each creature feared the other; each one's life depended upon the caribou. The wolf lived on the sick, the old, the emaciated – the Indian upon the fat, the strong, the healthy. And though each feared the other, the Indian respected Moisamadrook, the wolf, for his strength, his cunning, his fearlessness in darkness. And Moisamadrook, the wolf, respected the Indian for his dead-falls, his snares of caribou thong, and his arrows. But the Indian killed few wolves. Other furs were more lasting, like the seal and the otter. Some were more beautiful, like the marten and ermine. Most were easier to take. Especially the beaver.

'In turn, the wolf avoided the red man except during the fall and spring hunts when the Indian killed many caribou, more than he could use, leaving carcasses for Moisamadrook.

'But now, in the time of Beoth, the Indian, friend of the wolf and of all the wild, was gone, destroyed by the scourge that now threatened Beoth and Lupus and all the breed. A scourge of death.'

The wind increased. Boughs snapped around me. For a moment the voice was gone. I felt despair, yet my heart beat wildly as I thought of the track, and a vision of what must surely come filled my mind. Then the gust subsided, leaving branches hanging, swaying loosely in a gentle night.

I looked down at the fire, though I was warm. Wood had been added. My only need had been cared for. I was free to listen to the wind.

Again, as before, the murmur began, faintly distant, fading, then clearing, until the whisper broke from all around me – 'Wolf'.

'Beoth, the great grey wolf, grew and hunted and mated. He played with his pups and brought food for them to eat. Though his own father had been killed before his birth, Beoth from the first helped care for his offspring. Each year the white man destroyed many wolves and fewer and fewer were left to breed. Only in the interior wilderness were wolves to be found, and even here the white and the Micmac doggedly hunted, trapped, and killed.

'So it was that within a year from their birth the pups were destroyed, Beoth's mate was dead, and of the pack only Beoth and Lupus remained. Bounty killers had selfishly persevered until the very source was gone.

'Now Beoth and Lupus roamed together – Lupus, the old mother, dependent upon her strong offspring. Though her cunning guided the hunt, it was Beoth who killed. Though her knowledge often saved their lives, it was Beoth who destroyed the snares and sprang the traps.

'The two no longer killed the caribou unless an unfortunate crippled or sick animal wandered near. The old weakened wolf was no longer able to follow the herds. They fed on hare or roosting ptarmigan, depending upon their wit to capture them.

'Still, when the caribou began their trek the two wolves followed for a time, hoping, yet not daring, to attack. So they chanced on a caribou wounded by a hunter and relieved their gnawing hunger.

'Beoth lay resting on the bare side hill watching Lupus feed below him in the valley. The doe caribou had been fat and dry – choice meat after a diet of hare and partridge. The scent of man filled his nostrils, making them flare as he breathed out to weaken the poisoned air. He could not warn Lupus. The wolf must not howl in the presence of man, as an enemy. Lupus would certainly scent the danger in time.

'Beoth stood motionless, the hair of his back and neck rigid, low growls curling from the depths of his giant body. Lupus, busy with her meal, was eating steadily with her poor teeth and tired jaws. Lupus was shot and killed.

'Alone, Beoth began a great journey. Across lands unknown to him he trod, silent as death itself, the one last member of his breed. Across frozen lakes, over mountains and valleys, through marsh and forests – winter, spring, summer, fall – Beoth walked. No man would kill this great grey wolf. None could approach him. He carried all the cunning, intelligence, and dignity of his breed.

'Mating seasons came and passed. In the cold, pale light of the moon Beoth lifted voice to all his kind, yet found no mate.

'He wandered the land – and back – east to west, north to south – Doctors Hills, Lewis Hills, Blue Hills of Coteau, Lobster House, Mounts Peyton, Sylvester, and Sykes. He roamed, pausing to kill, to eat, to live.

'And somewhere, some time, death came to Beoth.

'Beoth, the grey wolf ghost, roams today over the same plateau, valley, and hill, through the same forests, stunted fir, and barren. His tracks are seen, and sometimes in the pale cold light Beoth, too, is seen.

'Death to the wolf is to roam and kill, somewhere in a living land. Beoth, the last, roams his land and that of all his kind. The land belongs to Beoth and to the Beothuk.

'What are the great rocks gleaming beneath the moon and stars? Boulders, you say, left from glaciers, relics, remnants of the past? Ah, no, they are markers. Count them – markers for all the wolves, the Indians, whose very breath you have stolen. Beoth paces now among them, on Mount St. Gregory, Bluie Hill and Soldiers Hill.

'There is no need to travel farther. You may return. Beoth cannot be pursued. By good fortune only, you may see the grey wolf ghost, and only by the full moon's light.'

Again the wind shatters the frozen branches above me. This time the flame flickers and suddenly rises to greater brightness. I am restless and walk around my camp, beyond the wavering light of the flames. Tracks all about me, all around the camp, approaching the edge of the early glow of the flame. Beoth, the grey wolf ghost. Was it the wind that spoke?

Now the flame is gone, dying to its natural embers as if no wood had been added, no greater flame burned. The wind has died. No breeze stirs as I move slowly towards my tent to rest.

Interlude

GULO

The Wolverine

One day the ice-world stopped. Once, ice had capped the globe like whitewash dripping from the poles, frozen miles deep. Now began the retreat, repeating the melting process of centuries before.

Bare land appeared. Thousands of years brought soil, plant, mammal, and bird back to the northern country. Lifeless, scoured rock altered, produced life, and so, with the help of sun and rain, became near-life, the almost-living soil.

Early, while ice yet covered the tip of the Great Northern Peninsula, plants grew along the south-west coast of Newfoundland. The mighty ice-bridge brought quadrupeds to the land. Then, even after the grip of freezing death had slackened, moving farther north, baring the land as an island, ice choked the Strait of Belle Isle much of the year and the bridge still remained, though it grew weaker. Today the bridge has gone. Occasionally the strait still clogs with great ice-pans, crushing to destruction in the warming springs of some years, but this is only a phantom bridge, a remembrance of the day when glaciers ruled.

For many thousands of years Alopex, the arctic fox, and Arctos, the polar bear, lived in Newfoundland. Today they drift to the land in error, trapped on pans, guided by ocean currents. With no ice-bridge, the strait became a barrier and served an opposite purpose, to separate and abandon. Thus the Beothuk, the Naskapi, the Montagnais, and the Eskimo would cross in dug-out and canoe of marvellous invention, but the four-footed creatures made contact by accident, on ice or floating debris.

The quadrupeds found their way to the island. The lynx arrived recently, and more may follow, though it becomes daily more difficult to compete for existence here. At first no mammals inhabited the ice-freed land. They came late, slowly over centuries, settled, and grew to become populations. Man, in his innocence, brought more creatures: moose, rats, mice, mink, hare, and shrew. Some were brought on purpose, some by accident. All of these were successful, and in their success competed at times with earlier creatures who had colonized without man's help.

How many came and failed to populate? Some came alone, only one of a kind, and so could not breed. Others came in numbers too few, too sparse, over too long a period, and became straggling failures, unable to adapt. Some fell prey to man.

The white man changed the landscape. Unlike the Beothuk before him, who lived from the soil, the water, and the forests, and left them but faintly scarred, the white settler burned, cut, ploughed, grazed, dammed, fished, hunted, trapped, poisoned, and built. Thus, both the presence of established mammals as competitors and the presence of man worked against the strange creature riding the floating pan towards shore.

Gulo heard the barking of the seals and lumbered towards the bight. He moved through spruce guarding the shoreline and across the final ramparts of ice piled deep by shifting seasons – the spring forcing its way into summer.

Phoca, the whitecoat, lay still on the pan. For several days the group of seals had drifted southwards, shifted from their northward migration. There were too few to attract the attention of the hunters steaming north into the mass of pack-ice where the great body of seals was to be found. This night, beneath a moonless, starlight sky, sometimes flaming brightly with curtains of Northern Lights snapping, whispering, fading, Gulo watched as Phoca drifted across the widening of the bight.

Indecision hampered Gulo's movement. He stood, then crouched. Minutes passed, as the wolverine lay motionless on the tortured ice. The only sounds were the snapping of the wispy, wavering light and the barking of a seal. Gulo bounded swiftly across the broken hummocks of the shoreline ice, across narrow ribbons of open water, around a widening swatch of it – on towards the whitecoat.

On the pan, at daylight, the land creature paced anxiously. Since the kill during the early-morning hours, the wind had shifted, and now, far from shore, Gulo worried the edges of the ice he was on. Adrift, he faced many fates: he might drown, starve, or be killed by landsmen looking for seals.

Gulo stayed on the pan as it cracked, split off, and caught up with others choking the great gulf. The pan then separated and drifted, shrinking away from the shore. During the day the wind blew harder. It whipped Gulo's coat apart, wrinkled it, parted it, blew it back. It drove the pan to the east. At night, the wind quietened, but the ice still boomed.

This was a strange world indeed, but Gulo did not swim for the world he had left. That land was gone. It had retreated into the fog before darkness. However, at dawn, Gulo found that his pan pressed tightly against the shore ice of a new land, and he clambered ashore.

The giant weasel – coarse-furred, clever, cowardly yet daring, with light stripes and eye-masks on a glossy brown – the wolverine, the carcajou, the devil dog: this was Gulo. Brother to the smallest living carnivore yet large enough to kill the deer when food was scarce, driven by man from familiar ranges, Gulo competed for life with lynx, fox, and wolf, and with lesser weasels. Like a small bear, feeding on insects and caribou, Gulo stole and plundered to live while his range became ever smaller.

He seldom visited the coasts now, where the vegetation was stunted by the wind and the cold. Lumbering up a ravine that led away from the sea-spray, Gulo hunted among the rocks and stunted trees. Farther inland, where the sea's cold influence weakened, the trees grew tall and dense. He humped past them into barren land where only alders and stunted fir grew. In a bog, he came upon a solitary mouse skittering across the crust snow, but he found no others. Gulo moved on.

Soon he encountered moose. He watched them, circled them, but never attacked. Sometimes he followed Vulpes, but when the red fox ran Gulo did not follow. Coming upon a wide brook, he turned to follow its banks and approached the area where a beaver worked close to his bank burrow. Here Gulo spent two days waiting, searching out the giant rodent. On the eve of the second day, he was rewarded by a visit from Ondra, the muskrat, who lived as a tenant of the beaver. Gulo fed and left, travelling to the east.

The white trapper worked the country from Trout River Ponds to the Hobblies. In the early 1930s, his main quarry was beaver, muskrat, and otter, although he still caught a few marten. Slips were set for fox and lynx, though he seldom took lynx these years. The man had four camps along his trap-line between Glenburnie and the Hobblies and he spent most of the winter in these camps away from home. His team of mongrel sled-dogs kept him company and he was able to kill a moose or a caribou often enough to satisfy the dogs and himself. He snared snowshoe hares and carried several hundred back to Glenburnie in winters when they were plentiful. There, his wife packed them in salmon tins, and later they were sold to augment the family's income.

Between the fish in the sea, the land animals, the land and sea birds, and the berries, the trapper maintained a reasonable standard of living, even when the depression forced most residents to go on the dole.

The trapper had never seen such an animal before. It was caught up in the middle by the slip, and signs in the snow told of the theft of bait and of an ensuing struggle. Gulo had circled the trap. Rather than enter through the obvious opening, he went in from the rear and ate the meat. But in creeping to the bait Gulo passed through the cleverly laid snare and was caught fast. Then, dragging the heavy fir pole, he made his way into the thick growth of stunted fir, where the man came upon him now. With his rifle, the trapper finished the injured wolverine. The pelt brought him $14.

Only one wolverine came. Now there are none left to come. Lands to the west, to the south, and to the north have lost the wolverine except in a few corners, isolated and almost unknown to man.

GUASHAWIT

The Bear

'We always went in the towers on the first of June. I mean official. But before June we'd pack in everything we was about to need. All the nails and felt and whatever we needed, my son, to fix up the cabin or tower or anything about. Some years the bears would have all the felt gone, the windows out, and the whole works a mess, my son, like you never saw.

'About May the fifteenth Jesse would come over and ask was I ready and I'd say I was itchy to get on with it, and I was too. So 'round then, 'round the middle of May now, we'd all go in. I always went into the Taubern Lake Tower. I was in 'er about twelve years altogether. In the summer, of course.

'It always took two weeks or more to git everything set up and right at the beginnin', that was the time to watch out for the bears, my son. When they comes out of the caves and the clumps they's hungry, my son. They'll eat anything in the world then, my sonnies.'

The old man's watery eyes held the faintest glint now. He crossed his legs, fished in his breast pocket behind the pencils for his tobacco and papers, and slowly rolled a cigarette. Leaning back, he placed a gnarled thumb beneath his right vest-strap and went on yarning. Between his left thumb and forefinger he held a roughly rolled cigarette with a wet end.

'I guess it was somewhere around the last of May, I was goin' up the ladder once a day or so to look about when I saw the bear away over the second rise a-pawin' on the ground at somethin'. I come on down and raffled about in me pack and picked out five shells and took the .30 and went back up to have another look. She was right there, still a-pawin' away, so I looked at me watch and I thought I'd just about have time to git down and git over to where she was and git back before dark, so off I went.

'My sonnies, you sees a long ways with dem glasses. When you set out to look up somethin' that you been watchin' from the glass, my sonnies, she's out there a wonderful long ways.

'Well, now, there was two little rises comin' up between the bigger ones and it took just about a half an hour to git over to where that bitch bear was feedin' and scratchin' about. I s'pose she was feedin' on, on the little emmets – and whatever she rooted up, the nish little grasses about, and, and anything at all.

'Now she was a big bitch bear. I squinted about a boulder on the last rise and could just see her back as she moved here and there, maybe, oh, just a good shot away for the .30, about a hundred yards maybe.

'So I got down swifflin' along the ground for a ways and then give a squint out at the bear again. Quick as a wink, my son, she jumped and ran off towards a patch of fir, so I up the gun and snaps off four shots so fast as I can operate her. I hit her all right. She wobbled a bit before she went in the firs. I runned over as quick as I could and just as I got there I hears somethin' at me side. There was a ledge droppin' a few feet to a yella bog below and so I went over and looked down and there was me bear runnin' along the ledge. I give her anudder, me last one. That was all the shells I had.

'In the mornin' I looked about from the tower and went over to the ledge where I fired at her but she warn't nowhere around. She was hit all right, but she kept on a-goin' so far as she could.'

The rock crevice reached into the earth for several feet and then widened where the rock became crumbly. Soil-forming mosses had plugged the light vents leading to ground-level above, but air still filtered through. It was dry in the crevice. Hard rains ran off the sloping rock-roof. It was seldom that a drop of water filtered through to the den-home.

Guashawit and his sister lay sleeping, curled around with noses hidden and covered between woolly hind legs. In February the little bears were tiny bundles a hundred times smaller than their mother. Now it was almost June and the cubs had grown to eight times their birth weight. The mother bear's cough disturbed the offspring. Quickly they moved against her, toothless gums nuzzling for teats. The mother dropped heavily to her side, blood bubbled from her nose and mouth as she laboured to force short breaths. The wound behind her shoulder was tiny. Only a few of the black hairs had been clipped by the bullet which smashed through the rib cage and settled snugly in the great creature's lung.

The beast lay motionless. Breathing became more difficult. The cubs suckled contentedly, eyes closed, and occasionally bumped the teats with mouth and nose, the better to grip the source of the rich, warm milk. Soon they were asleep.

Two hours passed. The mother bear breathed no longer. A small pool of drying blood lay on the floor of the den beneath her nose.

By morning the cubs were hungrier than they had ever been before. They returned to nurse time and again, but could no longer draw milk from the cold teats. They climbed over the mother, pulling her ears, pawing her nose and head. The adult bear had always retaliated at such actions. She certainly would not tolerate them now. But she did.

The two cubs squealed and whimpered when their attempts to wake the mother failed. They wrestled and fell asleep, each grasping the other, but soon their hunger wakened them.

They became restless, and nightfall found them exploring the cave entrance all the way to the out-of-doors, where they had always been forbidden to go.

'It warn't long after that I seen two cubs a-tumblin' over the marsh. They, they was small, nish lookin' little fellers almost too young to be about alone. And when I saw dem now I wondered, could it be the cubs from the old she-bear I hit a few days before?

'An' dat's just what they was now, my sonnies. Tiny, wee, little bears ain't never frolickin' about like that without the old bitch is with 'em. No, my son, that's just what happened. The poor little fellers got so hungry they was forced out to look for food.

'But, now, they was doin' all right. I watched 'em close and pretty soon a big hawk comes a-floatin' down off the barrens and give a swoop at one of the little fellers. My sonnies, how he did go! An' the, the other one stood up on the hind legs to face him, mind you!'

The old man pounded a fist into the cup of a hand and bent forward to emphasize his point. 'They did all right, my son.'

Another cigarette rolled and lit, a cup of tea from the steeping pot, and the old man with the leathery face and watery eyes leaned back. He drew a thick, crooked-fingered hand over his cheek and tugged at his chin and licked his lips and toothless gums.

'Well, now, it was only a day or so after, I seen 'em agin. They was eatin' away at the nish young shoots of grass and every so often they'd have a go at each other. Now, wasn't they de "cramp hands". Eatin' away and then they'd be at each other, quick as a flash.

'Then along about a hour or so after I first seen 'em, along comes a old she-bear with one cub. The cub was bigger than the two little fellers but it was still only a cub. Probably the

other cub had died maybe, or maybe she only had the one.
Sometimes a she will only have one cub, you know, and sometimes a she will have three. At first the little fellers ran but
when the old one didn't pay no attention to them they began
to come along closer to her. She never give a sign to 'em. Not
a sign, my son! Yet they went on almost to her and when she
walked on out of sight wit her cub the little fellers followed.'

To the cubs, the world was very big indeed. There was the
wind and all the objects never seen before. At first, when the
breeze bent a bush or parted the woolly fur on a cub's coat,
the little bears would cuddle the ground tightly and tremble.
They ate anything they saw or smelled, and so, from eating
old-year grasses with the new and many old-year berries, they
became ill. No small creature is safe from harmful bacteria
and the little bears lost weight. So they ate more and grew
worse.

On their third day alone a mother bear happened near
with her single cub. Guashawit and his sister saw them and,
trembling, they clamoured on shaky legs towards the bitch.
Close by they stopped. This was not their mother. They
backed away. The bitch paid no attention to the orphans
though she was aware of them.

The bigger cub bounded towards the twins and they
played, but the orphans were no match. Sickly and weak,
they bawled when tripped over or mauled by the larger
animal. The bitch bear grunted. She called to the three cubs.
They moved up to her and she nursed them all.

The adopted cubs grew swiftly. In four weeks' time they
were nearly as big as the bitch's own cub.

As they grew up together the cubs learned from the bitch
how to find the kinds of food they liked. They overturned
rotted logs to find beetles and beetle larvae. They ate ants
with sawdust and wood chips, and grasses, sedges, leaves,

berries, carrion, and mice. The adult showed them where to find honey and how to fish for the spawning salmon and trout.

Playful cubs learn quickly, but they would learn still more quickly if they were more attentive. Playing tag and wrestling in trees, on the ground, and in the water, the cubs would be alternately bruised and wet. One day, Guashawit had his ear torn by the bitch's playful cub. Blood oozed out and matted the woolly hair on Guashawit's neck and under his chin. The adult bear noticed the wound and with her powerful claws tore the bark of a fir tree, licked the pungent sap and transferred it to the little bear's ear.

Often the mother had to discipline her cubs, teaching them that foolishness can mean injury or death. Thus all three cubs often received heavy blows and cuffs from the mother bear, and, though they would whimper or bawl loudly at such times, they learned to respect the bitch and her lessons. When the bitch was ready to breed in the cubs' second year, the younger animals were prepared to live by themselves.

The cubs learned to feed on what was available at each season, so in the fall the bitch moved her tribe to the berry barrens where for several weeks they put on quantities of fat. As winter approached, the old bear sought a resting-place and found one beneath three trees that had fallen across each other in a blow-down area. There the bears made themselves comfortable, fashioning nest beds from grasses and sedges, in the hollows of the ground. Winter came and the bears slept.

By June of their second year the cubs were alone. The bitch had abandoned them, slapping them back and forcing them to stay behind. She would not return.

Guashawit travelled with his twin and the other cub until fall. Then he left them, the last of his playing days over. He spent the winter, except for a warm period of two weeks in January, under a windfall covered with snow.

In the spring, Guashawit travelled widely, seeking food of

any kind. His travels brought him to a woods camp. The camp had not yet been opened this spring, and careful woodsmen, thinking of bears, had boarded windows and doors of all the buildings. Sniffing around the buildings, Guashawit soon picked out the store-room and promptly began to tear the boards loose from the windows with his powerful forepaws.

One smash shattered the glass and Guashawit squeezed through, grunting. He was almost too big. Here was a barrel of salt meat, barrels of flour, tins of fruit and vegetables, and dried fruit. Guashawit bit into the cans and lapped at the draining juices, threw flour about with great sweeps of his forepaws and ate the salty meat and dried fruits. The dishes, stacked neatly on cupboard shelves, puzzled him and he picked them up and stacked them along the wall, breaking some in the process. Then, satisfied and filled, he broke down a door and left. Bears prefer to have separate entrances and exits, and, besides, Guashawit might well have been too big for the window now.

Guashawit destroyed parts of many camps in his lifetime. He was shot at and wounded, but balsam and spruce gum and water helped to heal his wounds.

Early each summer Guashawit sought out females ready to mate. Sometimes he fought other males. Great brawling battles he fought and won, for he was larger than any of the bears he fought.

Then, one late-summer day, Guashawit happened to roam near the place of his birth.

'You talk about bears! I'll tell you a bear story! It was the last year I was in at Taubern Lake and it was in the heat of the summer, August month it was. I'd only seen four or five bears all summer. One was around the camp and so I killed 'un. Late at night I got up and lookin' out the door I could just make 'un out, but I got 'un with one shot.'

The old man ran the back of his hand across his mouth and

recrossed his legs. 'But dat's another bear story. I saw this big bear from the tower early in the mornin'. He was a dog, I could see from his hump, and a big dog too. So down I got, grabbed me .30 and a pack, and off after him I goes. The bear was feedin' on berries now and this dog, my son, was busy takin' berries, bushes, and everything. I creeped up the last ways a-squintin' about each boulder to mark him down ahead and kinda watch his movements a bit. The wind, my sonnies, was just right, blowin' in to me, not real strong, but just shiftin' along quiet.

'An' when I peeked around the last rock, he was right there, boy, not fifty foot away an' eatin' the hurts berries so fast as he could gulp 'em down. He burped, my son, and you coulda heard it all the way to Port Blandford if the wind was right.

'So I ups me gun and aims right for the ear and squeezes and he jus' lops over, my son, as nice as you like it. A couple of twitches of the hind legs and he was quiet as a mouse. One shot, my sonnies!

'It was about the middle of the mornin' then and I took out me knife and panched 'im and skinned back off the hind quarters and scalped off the meat. My son, wasn't he fat now! Just like a pig. I stuffed the nish parts down in me pack and piled meat on top and packed it right out past the tower and out to the railroad. That's seven miles out from the tower, my son. I flagged down a speeder after a bit and went on in to Clarenville. Then, in the mornin' I went back in with Al, me son, and one of his buddies and they carried out some more. They was sixty pounds of meat in me pack and Al and his buddy took out just as much. The rest we had to leave because de heat was turnin' it.'

EPILOGUE

Fog weighted the late-summer leaves in the alder-bed. The world was small. No frost had yet weakened this year's green growth, but the ground already carried leaves faded by the summer's daytime heat and cool nights. A light mist penetrated the densest thickets about the alders' edge. The snowshoe rabbit lay huddled in its form, having ventured only to feed on a few birch leaves near by. The forest was soundless. Even the bird life was still this morning, save for the occasional call of a whitethroat that had not yet flown south.

A cow moose lay motionless with her calf, almost in sleep, resting. They had stayed in the area of the alder-bed and near-by cut-over since the calf was born. Many people had seen them, for they often ventured upon the grass of the city golf course to graze. Their pictures had been printed in a local paper.

He knew where to find the animals and on such a morning it was not difficult to move carefully and surprise them. He was soaking wet but, since there was no air stirring, he was not cold. Slowly the poacher walked along the tiny brook that snaked through the alders. Even when he accidentally broke the giant cow-parsnip, there was no noise this morning. The plant only leaned towards the ground and the sound it made was no louder than the poacher's foot sinking into the grass. When the moose heard the first noise, the intruder was only a hundred feet away. The huge, dim forms rose, and the poacher fired. Only the calf escaped, wounded.

The poacher sat down and rolled a cigarette, lit it, and took time to smoke it. He was alone. It was very still this morning and not even a jay appeared. His shots seemed dulled to him, yet they were heard by residents a mile away.

He went up to the moose. Expertly he cut open the stomach to the diaphragm, reached down, and cut out the liver. Then he removed the heart. Next he cut the oesophagus and larynx and pulled back, dumping the entrails and paunch to the ground. He took out the kidneys and removed the tongue. Now with his ax he split the backbone and rib-cage to the neck. His keen-edged knife sliced through the tough neck muscle and the skin, and the head was removed. Working his knife between the vertebrae, he disjointed the bone and halved each side. Then he removed each leg at the knee joint.

The poacher smoked another cigarette. He was sweating now from the activity of butchering. When he finished the cigarette he picked up a hind quarter with a rope sling and carried it down to the road a mile away. Here he cached it beneath some branches of slash from the cut-over fir. On the fourth trip he carried his rifle and ax. He picked a small fir standing close to the road and made two blaze marks on it and went home.